NAKED-EYE ASTRONOMY

NAKED-EYE ASTRONOMY

PATRICK MOORE, F.R.A.S.

Director of the Lunar Section,
British Astronomical Association
and
Director of the Armagh Planetarium, Ireland

Line diagrams by Warwick MacCallum

NEW YORK
W · W · NORTON *&* COMPANY · INC ·

COPYRIGHT © 1965 BY PATRICK MOORE

Library of Congress Catalog Card No. 65-27466

PRINTED IN THE UNITED STATES OF AMERICA

1 2 3 4 5 6 7 8 9

CONTENTS

LIST OF PLATES

Between pages 114 and 115

FOREWORD

AN astronomer is always pictured as a man with a telescope. Of course, this is natural enough; professional astronomers, intent upon studying remote stars and star-systems, depend entirely upon their telescopes, and would be more or less helpless without them. Even theoretical astronomers, who think in purely mathematical terms and who seldom see a telescope, would be starved of the basic information if they could not make use of photographs taken at great observatories.

On the other hand, it is not correct to say that telescopes are essential for every branch of astronomy; there are some ways in which the amateur enthusiast can make himself useful even if he has to rely upon his eyes alone. The opportunities for research are restricted, but they do exist. More important is the fact that the lack of a telescope does not debar the beginner from taking an active interest in what is happening up above. Suppose, for instance, that the newspapers contain a report that the planet Mars is at its closest to the Earth? It is easy enough to go out after dark and find Mars for oneself, which may not be scientifically valuable but which is certainly well worth doing. Then, too, the night sky seems to be crowded with stars, which make up various groups or constellations. These constellations may be identified without much trouble, and the stars become much more fascinating when the observer has learned which is which.

Astronomy has come very much to the fore in recent years, partly—but not, I think, entirely—because of the spectacular developments in rocketry and space research. Generally speaking, the beginner will acquaint himself with the fundamentals, decide which branch attracts him most, and then take steps to obtain a telescope. Yet there are plenty of people who will never go to such lengths, particularly as good telescopes tend to be expensive. It is for these "star-gazers" that I am writing; the present book is an attempt to show what may be done in astronomy without spending any money on equipment. I hope that some of those who read it will find it useful.

ACKNOWLEDGEMENTS

THERE ARE SEVERAL people to whom I owe a deep debt of gratitude for giving me their help during the compilation of this book. Henry Brinton and Robert Aylott were put to immense trouble in taking photographs for me, and have been responsible for most of the illustrations; the pictures of the solar eclipse were taken by the late Rudi Kühn, whose tragic death in a car accident is regretted by us all; the naked-eye drawings of the Moon were provided by Iain Nicolson, Terry Lock, Christopher Hardy and Pamela Pyer; the Leonid radiant by Colin Jack; and the plate showing the real nature of a constellation was taken with the help of Lawrence and Matthew Clarke as "reference points".

There is one special acknowledgement to be made. The line drawings, which make up an essential part of the book, were drawn entirely by Warwick MacCallum from my decidedly inexpert roughs. Without his skilful help, any value the book may have would have been drastically reduced.

Finally, I am most grateful to the publishers for all their help and encouragement—particularly to Martin Lewis and Michael Foxell.

PATRICK MOORE

East Grinstead,
June 21, 1965

NAKED-EYE ASTRONOMY

Chapter One

STAR-GAZING

HOW MANY STARS can you see on a dark, clear night? I once put this question to a group of a dozen people, none of whom knew anything about astronomy, and found that their guesses ranged from "ten thousand" up to "millions". In point of fact, nobody can ever see more than three thousand stars at any one moment without using optical aid, and the average number visible is less even than this. Appearances are deceptive.

Of course, any small telescope will alter the whole situation, and field-glasses or binoculars are not to be despised. Unfortunately, the newcomer to astronomy who wants to undertake some serious observation will find that an adequate telescope costs upward of £30, and unless he is really enthusiastic his career as an amateur astronomer may come to a speedy end. For the moment, let us assume that a telescope is unobtainable; in other words, let us put ourselves in the position of an astronomer of the pre-1609 period. The winter of 1609–10 is a landmark for the excellent reason that it was the time when Galileo, the great Italian scientist, first turned a telescope skyward, and so paved the way for modern astronomical research.

Though the ancient star-gazers had no telescopes, they managed to discover a remarkable number of facts. At an early stage, long before the birth of Christ, they realized that the Earth is a globe instead of being flat; they measured the Earth's size with considerable success; they drew up good star-catalogues, and they were well aware of the special character of the five "wandering stars" or planets, which were named Mercury, Venus, Mars, Jupiter and Saturn in honour of the pagan gods. They recognized that the Moon is our nearest neighbour in space, and they knew why it shows its regular phases, or apparent changes of shape from a crescent to a full disk. And much later, in the first two decades of the seventeenth century, the German mathematician Kepler

I

demonstrated that instead of the Sun going round the Earth, as most people had believed, the Earth moves round the Sun. Kepler could have taken this vital step even if telescopes had not appeared upon the scene at about the same time.

Before going into any details, it is, I think essential to give a brief outline of the basic astronomical facts. Most readers will know them already, but there is no harm in making sure, and the fundamentals may be summarized in a very few pages.

First, there is still some confusion between the science of astronomy on the one hand, and the mediæval hocus-pocus of astrology on the other. Actually, the two are as different as the proverbial chalk and cheese. Astronomy is the study of the universe; astrology, which purports to foretell human characters and destinies by observing the positions of the planets, is without any scientific foundation, and may be aptly summed up by the word "rubbish". I will return to astrology later, though to discuss it at any length would be a waste of time.

Secondly, we come at once to the problem of visualizing tremendous distances. The Earth is 93 million miles from the Sun; this may seem a long way, and by everyday standards it most certainly is, but to an astronomer it is not far. The universe is built upon a grand scale, and our Earth is a very tiny part of it.

The Sun is a star. It seems brilliant and splendid to us only because it is relatively near at hand; the stars visible at night-time are suns in their own right, many of them far larger and more luminous than the Sun we know, and appearing as faint, twinkling points only because they are so much further away. As for the Earth, it is a planet, travelling round the Sun in a path or orbit which is almost circular, and completing one full journey in $365\frac{1}{4}$ days. The Earth's diameter is almost 8,000 miles; that of the Sun is over 860,000 miles, so that if a million Earths were packed inside the Sun there would still be plenty of room to spare.

The Earth is not the only planet orbiting the Sun. As we have seen, the ancient sky-watchers knew of five more; since then an extra three (Uranus, Neptune and Pluto) have been added. The Moon is our own particular companion in space,

2

since it revolves round the Earth,[1] and at its distance of a mere 239,000 miles may be regarded as practically upon our doorstep. Technically, it is termed the Earth's satellite.

Together with various minor bodies, the Sun, Moon and planets make up what is known as the Solar System. The Sun is dominant, but we must always remember that the Solar System is nothing more than our "local village" in the universe. Even Pluto, the outermost planet, is very close when compared with the nearest of the so-called Fixed Stars.

Though the planets look like stars, they are fundamentally different. Like the Moon, they have no light of their own, and shine only because they reflect the rays of the Sun. The stars, on the other hand, are self-luminous globes of incandescent gas, sending out energy at a prodigious rate. Neither do they revolve round our Sun; why should they? Many of them are the Sun's peers.

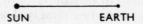

SUN   EARTH

Fig. 1. On this scale the nearest star will be four miles away.

To show the isolation of the Solar System in space, it may be useful to give a scale model, taking the Earth–Sun distance (93 million miles) as one inch. On this scale, the Moon will be no more than 1/400 of an inch from the Earth, while the distance between the Sun and the planet Pluto, which marks the boundary of the main Solar System, will be reduced to a little over three feet. On the same scale, the nearest star will be four miles off, and some of the bright stars to be seen on any cloudless night will have to be removed to tens, hundreds or even thousands of miles. We Earthmen are not nearly so important as we would like to believe.

Long before the telescope was invented, the old idea that the stars were fixed to a solid sky had been given up. However, it is true that the stars seem to stay in the same relative positions, whereas the planets wander about from one constellation to another. Consider, for instance, the group of seven

[1] To be strictly accurate, the Earth and Moon revolve round their common centre of gravity, but refinements of this sort need not concern us for the moment.

3

Fig. 2. The Plough has looked much the same since Classical times, and will still be the same in A.D. 3000.

fairly bright stars making up the Great Bear, known more commonly as the Plough (Fig. 2). The pattern is always the same; the Greek philosophers knew it, and so did the builders of the Egyptian Pyramids at the dawn of recorded history. Our remote descendants of, say, the year A.D. 3000 will still see the Great Bear looking virtually the same as it does now.

The stars are not truly fixed. They are moving about in space in all sorts of directions at all sorts of speeds, and over sufficiently long periods the constellation-patterns will alter; the tiny individual or "proper" motions of the stars are measurable, with modern instruments, from year to year. Yet these proper motions are so extremely slow that the naked-eye watcher is hopelessly unable to detect them over a lifetime, or even a hundred lifetimes. To all intents and purposes, we may regard the constellations as permanent.

The reason is not far to seek. An object which is a long way away will seem to be almost stationary, no matter how fast it is really moving—and the stars are almost inconceivably remote. The planets are comparatively near at hand, so that their individual shifts against the starry background show up over very short periods. Perhaps I may be allowed to repeat an analogy which I have given before, but which is, I think, useful. A bird flying above the tree-tops will seem to move much more quickly than a jet-aircraft at a height of several miles, even though its actual speed is so much less.

The star-system in which we lie is known as the Galaxy. It contains roughly a hundred thousand million stars, of which the Sun is one. Probably many of these stars have planet-families of their own, but there is no direct way of finding out, simply because no telescope in the world is powerful enough. No star (excluding the Sun, of course) can be seen as anything but a luminous dot; an attendant planet, shining only by light reflected from its parent star, would be much too faint to be seen at all. Indirect methods lead us to believe that the number of planet-families is large, but the only planets which we can actually see are those of our own Solar System, lit up by the Sun.

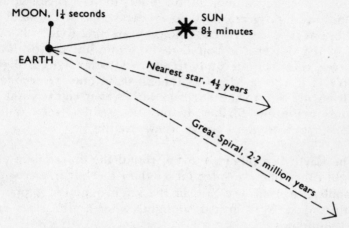

Fig. 3. Time taken by light to travel to or from other bodies.

Just as the Solar System is a very minor part of the Galaxy, so the Galaxy itself is a very minor part of the whole universe. Far away in space may be seen other galaxies, each containing their quota of thousands of millions of stars, but so remote that they appear as nothing more than dim, misty patches. From Europe, only one of these outer galaxies may be seen without a telescope. It is known as the Great Spiral in Andromeda, and it is the reverse of spectacular, but it has at least the distinction of being the most remote object ever visible with the naked eye. On our scale model, it must be placed some two million miles away from the speck representing the Earth.

Figures of this sort are quite defeating, and are impossible to appreciate, so that at this point it may be as well to introduce a new unit—the light-year. This is a measure not of time, but of length. It is based on the velocity of light, which amounts to 186,000 miles per second, and which has been measured with great precision.

If a ray of light covers 186,000 miles in each second, it will travel roughly 5,880,000,000,000 (almost 6 million million miles) in a year. This is the astronomer's "light-year", so that to convert light-years to miles, in round numbers, all that you need to do is to multiply by 6 million million. The nearest of the ordinary stars is 4 light-years away, which works out at approximately 24 million million miles; the Great Spiral lies at 2 million light-years, so that we are seeing it not as it is now, but as it used to be two million years ago. Evidently our view of the universe is bound to be somewhat out of date. However, this does not apply to our local Solar System; light can travel from the Moon to the Earth in only 1¼ seconds, and from the Sun to the Earth in rather over eight minutes.

Before going any further, it may be useful to set out the basic facts of astronomy under a few headings:

1. The Earth is a planet, moving round the Sun. There are eight other planets, some larger than the Earth and some smaller, orbiting the Sun in the same manner. A planet shines only by reflected sunlight, whereas the stars are self-luminous.

2. The Moon is the Earth's satellite, and is our nearest neighbour in space. Like the planets, it shines by reflected sunlight.

3. The Solar System consists of one star (the Sun), the nine planets, and various lesser bodies such as satellites. It is our home in the universe, which is the only reason why it seems so important to us.

4. The Sun is an ordinary star. It appears brilliant because it is so much closer to us than any other star.

5. The stars are suns. They do not revolve around our Sun, but lie far beyond the Solar System. They seem to keep the same relative positions in the sky, not because they are genuinely fixed, but because they are so remote that their apparent individual motions are negligible.

6. The Galaxy is the star-system which includes the Sun and the other members of the Solar System. There are about

100,000 million stars in the Galaxy, the nearest of which is 4 light-years away from us.

7. Other galaxies exist, so remote that their light takes millions of years to reach us. From Europe, only one external galaxy, the Great Spiral, is visible without a telescope.

So much, then, for fundamentals; there is nothing difficult about them. The next step must be to consider the changing aspects of the sky, just as the old star-gazers did so many centuries ago.

Chapter Two

THE CHANGING SKIES

WE LIVE UPON a spinning globe. The Earth is rotating all the time, carrying us with it; a full turn takes 23 hours 56 minutes, conventionally rounded off to 24 hours. We are not conscious of being whirled around, but the effects are obvious enough as soon as we look at the sky. Since the Earth's direction of spin is from west to east, the heavens appear to rotate from east to west, carrying the Sun, Moon, planets and stars with them.

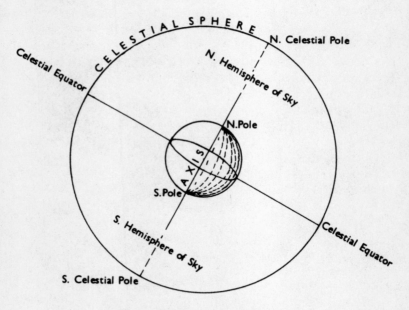

Fig. 4. The Celestial Sphere.

The celestial bodies, then, always seem to be in motion. There is one exception; the fairly bright Polaris, the Pole Star, keeps almost stationary, so that its position in the sky is constant. From England, its altitude above the horizon is

8

rather more than 50 degrees. Polaris is in a special place; everything else moves round it, making one circuit in 24 hours.

This peculiarity has nothing whatsoever to do with Polaris itself. It so happens that the star lies almost at the north pole of the sky, but it has not always done so; in ancient times, when the Egyptian Pyramids were built, the north celestial pole was marked by the much fainter star Thuban. Moreover, Polaris is not exactly at the polar point. It describes a small daily circle round the true pole, though casual observers are not likely to notice its shift.

The diagram in Fig. 4 should make the situation clear. The Earth is shown in the centre, with its two poles, the equator, and the axis of rotation. For convenience, it may be supposed that the "celestial sphere" is solid, with the stars fixed on to it. The axis points northward to the North Celestial Pole, within one degree of Polaris; the South Celestial Pole is not marked by any bright star, to the constant regret of Australians and New Zealanders. And just as the Earth's equator divides the globe into two hemispheres, so the celestial equator halves the sky.

Quite obviously, the South Celestial Pole will never be visible from a northern country, such as Britain. The solid body of the Earth gets in the way, so that the southernmost stars never rise above the horizon. On the other hand, the stars close to Polaris will never set, and will always be visible whenever the sky is sufficiently dark and clear. The Great Bear, most famous of all groups, comes into this category. It sweeps round the pole, and even when at its lowest it is still well above the horizon, so that it is said to be *circumpolar*. The brilliant orange star Arcturus, which lies further south in the sky, is not circumpolar; at its lowest it drops below the horizon, so that it rises and sets regularly.

Anyone who travels from England toward the Earth's equator will notice that the altitude of Polaris is becoming less. Go to Mexico or Central India, for example, and the angle between Polaris and the horizon will be reduced to only 20 degrees. This means that the Great Bear will no longer be circumpolar, since part of its daily circle will lie below the horizon. To compensate for this, southern stars which never rise in Britain

9

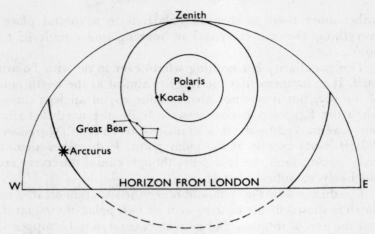

Fig. 5. Kocab, a star not far from Polaris, describes a small circle. The Great Bear, farther from Polaris, never sets, but can reach the zenith or overhead point. Arcturus can pass below the horizon, and so is not circumpolar.

will have come into view—notably the brilliant yellow Canopus, which is never to be seen from Europe, but which rises well into the Mexican sky.

Go to the equator, and you will find that Polaris lies right on the horizon; the South Celestial Pole is situated on the opposite horizon, and the Celestial Equator passes overhead, so that the entire sky is visible at one time or another. In the Earth's southern hemisphere Polaris is lost to view, and from Australia even the Great Bear has gone. However, Australian skies are graced by glorious constellations such as the Southern Cross, which is circumpolar over the whole continent.

In the present book I propose to devote considerable space to star recognition, but I find myself in a difficulty at once, because the charts needed by northern and southern observers will not be the same. All I can do is to write from the viewpoint of the northerner, with due apologies to any reader who happens to live in the Antipodes. Meanwhile, I must say something about the bodies of the Solar System, which take part in the daily rotation of the sky, but which have marked individual shifts of their own.

The Sun appears to travel right round the sky in the course of one year. Its light completely drowns the stars, though

accurately-pointed telescopes will show some of them; only on
rare occasions, when the Moon passes in front of the bright
solar disk and blots it out for a few minutes, can the naked-eye
watcher see stars during the daytime. The Sun's yearly path
among the constellations is known as the ecliptic,[1] and lies
partly north and partly south of the celestial equator. The belt
in the sky centred upon the ecliptic is termed the Zodiac.

The old star-gazers knew that the five bright planets are

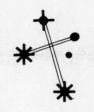

Fig. 6. The Southern Cross. This
glorious constellation, with its bright
pointer stars in Centaurus, can never
rise from Europe or the United States
but is circumpolar in Australia, as it
lies relatively near the South Celestial
Pole.

always to be found somewhere in the Zodiac, and can never
wander away from it; for instance, no planet ever strays as far
as the region of the Great Bear. The reason is that the orbits
of the planets round the Sun are in much the same plane, so
that if we draw a plan of the Solar System upon a flat sheet
of paper we are not far wrong. The error amounts to 7 degrees
for Mercury and less than 4 degrees for the other planets
(apart from Pluto, which is much too dim to be seen with the
naked eye, and was discovered as recently as 1930). In the
diagram (Fig. 7) an observer on Earth may see various
planets in direction A or B, but will never see them toward C
or D. The same applies to the Moon.

Because the planets move about, it is impossible to enter
them upon a set of permanent star-charts. Fortunately they

---

[1] The ecliptic should be defined as "the plane of the Earth's orbit projected upon
the celestial sphere", but this comes to much the same thing.

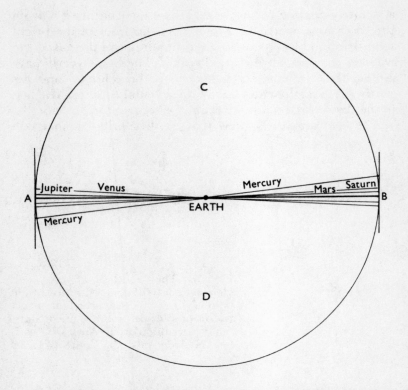

Fig. 7. All the bright planets have slight orbital inclinations to the main plane of the Solar System ($7°$ for Mercury, $3\frac{1}{2}°$ for Venus, less than $3°$ for Mars, Jupiter and Saturn) so that they can be seen only near the ecliptic; in other words they keep to the Zodiac (A B) and can never be seen toward C or D.

are easy to recognize, partly because they are confined to the Zodiac and partly because each planet has its own characteristics. Mercury need not concern us for the moment, because it is never conspicuous, and the casual observer is unlikely to notice it at all. Venus and Jupiter are so brilliant that they outshine any star, while Mars is distinguished by its strong red colour. Saturn is the only planet which can look confusingly like a star, but its movements are slow, and it remains in the same constellation for months at a time.

There is an easy way to show the general movement of the sky, open to anyone who possesses an ordinary camera capable of giving a time-exposure. Take a picture of the night sky, leaving the shutter open for some time, and you will obtain a series of trails as the stars track across the field. Pointing the camera at the celestial pole means that you will be able to pinpoint the actual polar point (Plate I); and by giving various exposure, you can make the star trails longer and longer (Plates II and III). To take a picture showing the stars as sharp points, it is necessary to drive the camera so as to compensate for the rotation of the sky, which means using a special driving mechanism (Plate II*a*). This is, surely, the most convincing possible demonstration of the fact that the Earth is rotating.

Apart from the circumpolar groups, the constellations are seasonal; thus the glorious Orion is high on winter evenings, but cannot be seen at all near midsummer, because the Sun lies too close to it. The skies are always changing, and each month brings its quota of interesting objects. Astronomy can never be dull.

Chapter Three

PATTERNS OF STARS

THE FIRST THING that strikes one about the night sky is that the stars seem to form patterns. Early men were suitably impressed, and divided the stars into groups or constellations, giving each constellation a separate name. The system which has come down to us is that of the Greeks, who drew up star-catalogues in which they recognized a grand total of 48 constellations. The list has been extended since, and nowadays the official maps show almost ninety groups of various shapes and sizes.

The original constellations were named after living creatures, every-day objects, or mythological gods and heroes. It has been said that the sky is a vast art-gallery; we may see Hercules, Orion the Hunter and the gallant youth Perseus, to say nothing of the Winged Horse, the Scorpion, the Swan, the Triangle and the Cup. It must be added that very few of the constellations bear the slightest resemblance to the objects which they are supposed to represent. For instance, the stars of the Swan form a large and rather lop-sided cross, while the Winged Horse is simply a square[1] and Hercules has no real shape at all. However, the ancients—like modern "painters" of the surrealist school!—were nothing if not imaginative, and constellations such as the Telescope and the Air-Pump, added to the

Fig. 8. Orion.

[1] In the literal, not the metaphorical, sense!

14

sky by later astronomers, seem very unromantic in comparison.

Though the old constellations are Greek, they are known today by their Latin names. The Swan is "Cygnus", the Great Bear "Ursa Major", and so on. Many books written for newcomers to astronomy make use of the English names, but to me this seems a cowardly evasion; as the Latin versions are used in all scientific work, why not become used to them at once? It is not as though they are in the least tongue-twisting. I have therefore kept to Latin, though on page 20 I have listed the English equiva-lents as well.

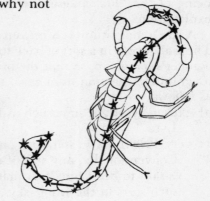

The names of individual stars are generally of Ara-bic origin. Many people have heard of Sirius in Canis Major (the Great Dog), Arcturus in Boötes (the Herdsman), and so on. This is all very well, but it would be impossible to remember names for all the naked-eye stars, and in 1603 the German astronomer Bayer pro-posed a much more con-venient system.

Fig. 9. Scorpio, the Scorpion.

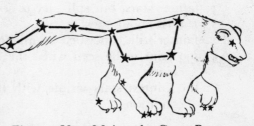

Fig. 10. Ursa Major, the Great Bear.

What Bayer did was to take each constellation separately, and give its stars Greek letters. The first three letters of the Greek alphabet are Alpha, Beta and Gamma; thus the brightest star in the constellation would be Alpha, the second Beta, the third Gamma, and so on down to Omega. The Greek letter is followed by the name of the constellation in which the star lies, written in the genitive, so that the brightest star in Cygnus becomes Alpha Cygni (= Alpha of the Swan), while Sirius, the leader of Canis Major, is Alpha Canis Majoris (= Alpha of the Great Dog). The system has its weaknesses, but it has stood the test of time, and has become firmly established.⟩

About 200 stars have names of their own, but most of them have become obsolete, and I propose to ignore them. Only the two dozen brightest stars have proper names which are still fashionable. These exceptionally brilliant stars are reckoned as being of the "first magnitude", a term which needs a little explanation.

A star's magnitude is a measure of its apparent brightness. The scale works in a sort of back to front way, in the manner of a golfer's handicap, so that the brightest stars have the lowest magnitudes. Starting from zero, the appearances are roughly as follows:

0: extremely bright stars such as Rigel in Orion and Vega in Lyra.

1: very bright stars, standing out among their neighbours. Conventionally, any star of magnitude brighter than $1\frac{1}{2}$ is said to be of the "first magnitude"; there are only 21 such stars in the whole sky.

2: moderately bright stars, such as Polaris and the six senior members of the Great Bear.

3: fainter stars, but still easy to see even when there is some mist about.

4: fainter still, concealed by mist or moonlight.

5: too faint to be seen when the sky is not really dark and clear.

6: the faintest stars visible with the naked eye under good conditions.

The scale may be extended both ways. Venus, the brightest planet, is so brilliant that its magnitude is *minus* 4, while on the other hand the world's largest telescope can record stars as faint as magnitude *plus* 23. Astronomers can measure magnitudes very accurately, but the naked-eye observer will be well content with a value given to the nearest tenth. Thus Gamma Ursæ Majoris, one of the stars in the Great Bear, has a magnitude of 2·4, roughly half-way between 2 and 3.

Note that a star's magnitude has nothing directly to do with its real luminosity. A star may shine brilliantly in our skies either because it is relatively close, or because it is genuinely very powerful. Sirius, with a magnitude of *minus* 1·4, is much the brightest star, but it is also one of our nearest stellar neighbours, and is "only" 26 times more luminous than the Sun. Rigel in Orion is equal to perhaps 50,000 Suns put together, but it is so much more remote that it does not appear so bright as Sirius. Ideas of this kind were quite beyond the mental range of ancient astronomers, who thought that the stars were equally distant from us, and were lamps fixed on to a solid celestial sphere.

Another point which would have taken our ancestors by surprise is that what we term a "constellation" is not made up of stars which are truly associated with each other. We are dealing with a mere line-of-sight effect, since the various stars in any particular constellation may be at quite different distances from us. As an example, consider Cygnus (the Swan), which is know popularly as the Northern Cross because of the arrangement of its five chief stars.

Deneb or Alpha Cygni, the brightest of the five, is of the first magnitude, or, more precisely, 1·3; of the rest Gamma is of magnitude 2·2, Epsilon 2·5, Delta 2·9 and Beta 3·1. (Here, as often happens, the brilliancy sequence has become out of order; Beta should really be the second brightest star in the constellation, not the fifth.) Cygnus is easy to find, and is very prominent in the summer sky. But when we examine the real distances of the five stars, we realize that they are in no way connected with each other. Epsilon is 74 light-years from us, Delta 270, Beta 410, Gamma 750 and Deneb as much as 1600. The stars of the group simply happen to lie in the same part of the sky as seen from the Earth, and in fact Deneb is much further away from Delta or Beta than we are. The diagram (Fig. 11) which is drawn to scale, drives this point home. See also Plate IV, which shows an instructive model.

A constellation, then, is not a true group at all. The patterns which we see are purely fortuitous; if our home lay in another part of the Galaxy, the patterns would be different.

I cannot resist making a slight digression here in order to dispose of astrology, the so-called science according to which the positions of the planets affect the lives and characters of human beings. Suppose, for instance, that when a baby is born, the planet Mars is in the constellation of Scorpio (the

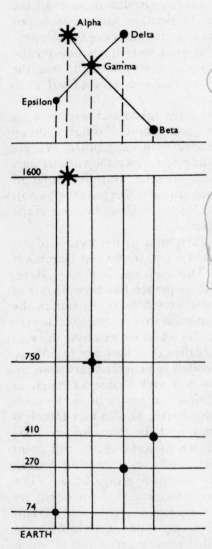

Fig. 11. Relative distances from Earth of the five stars in the Cross of Cygnus.

Scorpion). Astrologers claim that this will have profound effects upon the child. Yet what precisely is meant by saying that a planet is "in" a constellation?

Planets are very near us in comparison with the stars; as has been pointed out earlier, a scale model in which the Earth-Sun distance is taken as one inch will mean moving the nearest star out to four miles. To talk about a planet being "in" a constellation means simply that the planet is seen against a background of unassociated stars which have been arbitrarily grouped into a pattern and given a name. It is rather like holding up a penny in front of a cloud background and then claiming that the penny is "in the clouds". Taxed with arguments of this kind, astrologers will usually retire baffled, muttering in their beards about Ancient Teachings and Esoteric Influences. No more need be said.

From time to time there have been suggestions that the whole sky-map should be revised, with the introduction of a new set of constellations which would be more logical and more convenient. It is quite true that the present system is chaotic. Vast snakes sprawl among fishes, bears and birds; one constellation (Serpens, the Serpent) is made up of two separated parts, and there are some groups which certainly do not merit separate names, notably Leo Minor (the Little Lion), which is marked by a few very faint stars and looks nothing like the shape of a lion or anything else. However, the various bright ideas have fallen upon deaf ears, which is on the whole just as well. One particularly hideous suggestion was to re-name the constellations in honour of political leaders. This would have caused inevitable repercussions; how long would it take the United Nations authorities to decide whether a particular star should be included in, say, General de Gaulle or Senator Goldwater? Mythological names are safer.

Apart from the circumpolar groups, the constellations are seasonal. In winter evenings Orion is high in the south, and dominates that part of the sky, but in summer it cannot be seen at all. In drawing up a list of the constellations visible from Britain and the northern United States (see overleaf), I have therefore given them under seasonal headings, so that, for instance, a constellation given in the "winter" column is at its best during evenings from December to February—even though it may be seen at other times also.

The list may seem formidable, but it is not really so. It takes only a little practice for the observer to learn one group from another, and the beginner who is willing to spend a nightly ten minutes or so outdoors for a few weeks should have little trouble. It is much easier to learn the constellations, uneven and tortuous though they may be, than to learn one's way around the maze of streets in modern London.

THE CONSTELLATIONS

This list includes all the groups visible in Europe and the northern United States, though some of them (Argo Navis, Scorpio and Eridanus, for example) do not wholly rise; only a small portion of Argo may be seen. Particularly important constellations are marked with an asterisk.

Circumpolar

Camelopardus:	the Giraffe.	Lacerta:	the Lizard.
Canes Venatici:	the Hunting Dogs.	Lynx:	the Lynx.
*Cassiopeia:	Cassiopeia.	*Ursa Major:	the Great Bear.
Cepheus:	Cepheus.	Ursa Minor:	the Little Bear.
Draco:	the Dragon.		

Spring

*Boötes:	the Herdsman.	Hydra:	the Watersnake.
Cancer:	the Crab.	*Leo:	the Lion.
Coma Berenices:	Berenice's Hair.	Leo Minor:	the Little Lion.
Corona Borealis:	the Northern Crown.	Sextans:	the Sextant.

Summer

*Aquila:	the Eagle.	Ophiuchus:	the Serpent-Bearer.
Corvus:	the Crow.	Sagitta:	the Arrow.
Crater:	the Cup.	*Sagittarius:	the Archer.
*Cygnus:	the Swan.	*Scorpio:	the Scorpion.
Delphinus:	the Dolphin.	Scutum:	the Shield.
Equuleus:	the Little Horse.	Serpens:	the Serpent.
Hercules:	Hercules.	*Virgo:	the Virgin.
Libra:	the Balance.	Vulpecula:	the Fox.
*Lyra:	the Lyre.		

PATTERNS OF STARS

Autumn

*Andromeda: Andromeda.
Aquarius: the Water-Bearer.
Aries: the Ram.
Capricornus: the Sea-Goat.
Cetus: the Whale.
*Pegasus: the Winged Horse.

*Perseus: Perseus.
Pisces: the Fishes.
Piscis
  Austrinus: the Southern Fish.
Triangulum: the Triangle.

Winter

Argo Navis: the Ship Argo.
*Auriga: the Charioteer.
*Canis Major: the Great Dog.
Canis Minor: the Little Dog.
Columba: the Dove.
Eridanus: the River.

*Gemini: the Twins.
Lepus: the Hare.
Monoceros: the Unicorn.
*Orion: Orion.
Sculptor: the Sculptor.
*Taurus: the Bull.

THE GREEK ALPHABET

α	Alpha	ν	Nu
β	Beta	ξ	Xi
γ	Gamma	o	Omicron
δ	Delta	π	Pi
ε	Epsilon	ρ	Rho
ζ	Zeta	σ	Sigma
η	Eta	τ	Tau
θ	Theta	υ	Upsilon
ι	Iota	φ	Phi
κ	Kappa	χ	Chi
λ	Lambda	ψ	Psi
μ	Mu	ω	Omega

Chapter Four

THE VARIETY OF THE STARS

TO THE CASUAL observer, one star looks very much like another; there are differences in brilliancy, but that is all. Yet closer inspection shows that the stars are by no means all the same.

One thing in common to them all is that they are subject to twinkling, or—to use the scientific term—scintillation. The old rhyme which begins "Twinkle, twinkle, little star" is certainly graphic, and on dark, clear nights the effect is very marked. A brilliant star low down in the sky may flash violently, looking red, green and white in turn.

Twinkling has nothing whatsoever to do with the stars themselves. We are observing them through the whole thickness of the Earth's atmosphere, which is always unsteady; a star appears as a point of light, with no measurable disk, so that it seems to "wobble" and flicker. Were it possible to observe from above the atmosphere, as modern space-men have done, the twinkling would vanish, and the star would shine steadily. When men reach the Moon, which has no atmosphere worth mentioning, they will see the stars as hard, steely dots.

The cause of twinkling has been known for a long time, and in any case there is an easy way to show that the Earth's air is responsible. Watch a bright star which is low down; it will flash strongly. Then compare it with a star which is of equal brilliancy, but is high above the horizon. You will find that the higher star twinkles much less.

It is often said that planets, unlike stars, do not twinkle, so that they may be recognized in this way alone. Admittedly the planets twinkle less than the stars, because a planet is not a mere point; it shows a definite disk, and the scintillation effects over the different parts of the disk tend to cancel each other out. On the other hand, it is worth noting that a planet low over the horizon may twinkle quite strongly. Mercury is particularly subject to it.

A star, as we have seen, is a globe of incandescent gas, shining by its own light and producing an amazing amount of energy. It is not "burning" in the ordinary sense of the word; oddly enough, it is too hot to burn. The Sun has a surface temperature of 6,000 degrees Centrigrade, while near its centre the temperature is believed to rise to the staggering value of more than 13 million degrees Centigrade. Were the Sun made up of coal, and burning fiercely enough to emit as much energy as the real Sun actually does, it would destroy itself in a comparatively short time. It could not last for more than a million years or so, whereas the age of the real Sun is greater than 5,000 million years.

Modern astronomy has solved the problem, at least in part. Exact details remain to be cleared up, but we may be sure that a star radiates by means of what is termed "nuclear transformation"—or, in a broad sense, atomic energy. Moreover, the stars show a wide range of luminosity and temperature, so that they are not all of the same colour. The Sun, as anyone can see, is yellow; a star with a cooler surface will be orange or orange-red, while a hotter star will be white or bluish. The very hottest stars have surface temperatures of over 30,000 degrees Centigrade, while at the other end of the scale there are red stars with surfaces at a relatively mild 2,500 degrees or so. (This does not mean that all red stars are faint. Some of them are of tremendous size, so that their total luminosities are much greater than that of the hotter but smaller Sun.)

Use a telescope, or even a pair of binoculars, and these diverse colours will be well seen; for instance Vega, the brilliant star which is almost overhead during summer evenings, is strongly blue, while Betelgeux in Orion has been compared with a red, glowing coal. Unfortunately the colours are not very obvious to the naked eye. All that can really be said is that a few stars are clearly orange or orange-red, while some of the brighter ones have a bluish cast; the rest simply look white. I shall have more to say about this later on.

Of the special kinds of stars, the most spectacular are the doubles. The best example is Mizar, the second star of the Great Bear's tail—or the handle of the Plough, whichever name is being used for the group. When the sky is dark and

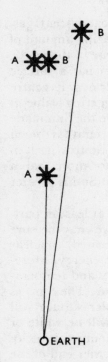

Fig. 12. Optical Double Stars (left). Actual distances; B is much more remote than A. (Right) Appearance as seen from Earth, with A and B close together.

clear, Mizar is seen to have a much fainter star, Alcor, close beside it. Telescopically Mizar itself may be split into two components, so close together that to the naked eye they appear as one mass.

Many thousands of double stars are known. Some of them are due to line-of-sight effects, since if one star lies almost behind another, as seen from Earth, the two will appear side by side in the sky (Fig. 12). Yet oddly enough, these non-related or "optical" pairs are in the minority. Usually, the two components of a double star are genuinely associated, and are moving round each other much as the two bells of a dumb-bell will move when twisted by the bar which joins them. A system of this sort is known as a "binary". If the components are close together, it will take only a few hours for the two stars to complete a full revolution; if the components are wide apart, the revolution period may amount to millions of years.

We are not concerned here with telescopic binaries, and, obviously, all double stars which are wide enough to be split with the naked eye must be either optical pairs, or else binaries with very long periods. One odd fact which has emerged from modern research is that binary systems are remarkably common, and may even be the rule rather than the exception, so that they outnumber single stars such as our Sun. Triple stars, quadruple stars and still more complex groups are known, and have been termed "family parties" of stars. It used to be thought that a binary was produced by the break-up of a single star, but nowadays most astronomers regard this theory with distaste, and it is considered more likely that the components of a binary were formed independently, at much the same time and in the same region of space.

24

Next we come to variable stars, which change in brightness over short periods of time. They are not so common as binaries, but by now many thousands have been listed, and scientifically they are of great importance.

An ordinary star will shine steadily for millions of years at a time. The Sun has not changed much since the Earth was formed, between 4,000 and 5,000 million years ago, and it is not likely to alter for thousands of millions of years yet, which is lucky for us; even a slight change in the Sun's output would have disastrous results for life on Earth, so that we would be either fried or frozen. It is quite possible that the Ice Ages which have occurred now and then throughout geological history have been due to slight reductions in the amount of energy sent out by the Sun, but even if this theory is correct it does not make the Sun a variable star in the usual sense of the term.

A real variable shows short-term changes. For a few days, or a few weeks or months, it brightens; it reaches its maximum, and then it fades once more, reaching minimum brilliancy before starting to increase once more. The interval between one maximum and the next is known as the star's period. When these changes are plotted on a chart, showing brightness (magnitude) against time, the result is called a light-curve—and in most cases the light-curve is regular. Variables of short

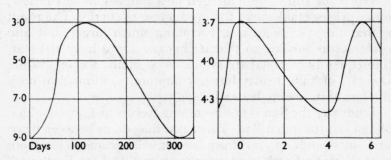

Fig. 13. Light-curves of Mira Ceti (left) and Delta Cephei (right).

period, usually called Cepheids, repeat their changes time and time again with no alteration in period, maximum magnitude or minimum magnitude. Where the period is longer, amounting to several months, it is found that the behaviour is less precise, so that these long-period stars are fundamentally different from the Cepheids. There are also irregular variables, whose changes cannot be predicted, and which are always apt to catch observers by surprise.

So far as we can tell, a variable is not in the placid, stable condition of a normal star. It "pulsates", swelling and shrinking, and changing in luminosity. One famous variable, Mira, has a period of about 331 days, and is a conspicuous naked-eye object when at its best, though at minimum it becomes so faint that even binoculars will not show it.

This may be the moment to elaborate slightly upon the life-story of a star. If modern theories are correct, a star begins its career by condensing out of a cloud of gas and dust in space. As it shrinks, by gravitational attraction, its inner parts become hot; when the temperature has risen sufficiently, energy production begins, so that the star starts to shine. Its main "fuel" is hydrogen, the lightest of all gases and by far the most plentiful substance in the whole universe. By nuclear transformation, hydrogen is changed into another gas, helium, with the emission of radiation and considerable loss of mass. The Sun is losing mass at the rate of 4 million tons a second. This seems alarmingly high, but we need have no fears, since the Sun's vast globe contains enough hydrogen to last it for a long time yet.

When the supply of hydrogen in a star begins to run low, other processes take over the production of energy. The result is that the star swells out, becoming much larger, but also cooler at its surface, so that it changes into a huge red star. Subsequently it collapses into a very small, feeble "White Dwarf", of high density but low luminosity, shining on until the last of its energy leaves it.

Evidently the Sun is not becoming feebler as it grows older. When it turns into a Red Giant, as it may do in between 8,000 and 10,000 million years from now, it will become so luminous that all life on Earth must come to an end, and the Earth itself may perish. Heat, not cold, will be our eventual downfall—so far as we can tell, though of course we may be completely wrong.

Linked with the whole problem of stellar evolution are the strange, spectacular "novæ", or temporary stars. Occasionally a star will be seen where no star had been visible before; the newcomer may shine brightly for a few days or weeks, but then it will fade away and pass beyond the range of the naked-eye observer. Before telescopes were invented, it was thought that a nova must be genuinely new. However, it has now been found that instead of being freshly-created, a nova is merely a faint star which suffers a tremendous outburst, affecting its outer layers and causing it to flare up. The energy-producing mechanism becomes out of control, so to speak, and the results are violent, though after the outburst is over the star returns to its former state.

Telescopic novæ are not infrequent, but those visible with the naked eye are much rarer. The last really bright example was the nova of 1942; for a few days it surpassed any of the stars in the Great Bear, but by now it has become so faint that a large telescope is needed to show it.

If our Sun burst out in this way, the Earth would be destroyed at once, but fortunately nothing of the sort is likely to happen, since stars of solar type are reassuringly stable and well-behaved. It has been suggested that every star becomes a nova at a late stage in its career, but we do not really know.

Even greater outbursts occur now and then. With a "supernova", the star blows much of its material away into space in a cataclysmic explosion, producing as much energy as millions of Suns put together. Unlike a normal nova, the star never returns to its old state, and seems to end up as a mass of expanding gas. No supernova has appeared in our own Galaxy since 1604, a few years before telescopes appeared on the scene. Astronomers regret this, since they would very much like to study a supernova with the aid of modern equipment, but at least they can use their large telescopes to trace and study supernovæ which flare up in other galaxies millions of light-years away.

It used to be thought that a nova or supernova might be the result of two stars colliding head-on. This idea seemed logical enough—until it became possible to measure the size of the Galaxy. Not surprisingly, the stars proved to be widely separated in space, and we now know that collisions must be excessively rare.

Yet genuine groups of stars do occur. These are termed

clusters, a name which sums them up perfectly. The most famous of them is known popularly as the Seven Sisters, though officially as the Pleiades. It lies in the constellation of Taurus (the Bull), and is a prominent naked-eye object; at first sight it looks like a hazy patch, but normal-sighted people can make out six or seven separate stars, while binoculars will show many more. Altogether, there are over 200 stars in the cluster. Both the Pleiades and another famous cluster, the Hyades, are shown in Plate VI.

The stars in a cluster are more closely packed than in an ordinary region of space. Of course, they are further apart than they look; everything in the universe is upon a vast scale, and the various members of the Pleiades are still many thousands of millions of miles away from each other. Open or "loose" clusters of this sort are common enough, though not many of them are visible without optical aid.

Rather different are the globular clusters, whose outlines are much more regular. They look almost round; telescopes will show separate stars near their edges, but closer to the centre the crowding is much greater, and a large instrument is needed to resolve the glowing mass into stars. Globular clusters lie near the edge of the Galaxy, and so are a long way off, which results in their being comparatively faint objects. Three are visible with the naked eye, but unfortunately only one rises above the horizon in Europe. This is the Great Globular in Hercules, about which I shall have more to say on page 125.

If our Sun, with its family of planets, were a member of a globular cluster, the night skies would be glorious indeed. There would be many stars shining more brilliantly than Venus does to us; true darkness would be unknown, and even when the Sun and Moon were out of view the heavens would seem to be ablaze. Of course, it is very probable that some of the stars in globular clusters have planetary systems of their own, and that some of these planets are inhabited, though we we have no definite proof.

Nebulæ come into another category altogether. The Latin word "nebula" means "cloud", and the dim, misty patches of light in the night sky known to astronomers as nebulæ do look just like faint, luminous clouds. All things considered, the name is not at all inappropriate. A nebula is indeed a cloud, made up of thin gas and finely-spread material. One splendid example lies in the Sword of Orion, below the three bright stars of the so-called Hunter's Belt. The Orion Nebula is easy to see with the naked eye, and has been known for centuries.

Nebulæ are particularly interesting because they are thought to be stellar birthplaces. A star begins its career by condensing out of interstellar material—and what more suitable place could there be than a nebula? Thousands of millions of years ago, our Sun must have been born in such a way.

Before astronomy entered its latest phase, less than fifty years ago, all nebulæ were thought to be members of the Galaxy. Then came a spectacular discovery. The gas-and-dust nebulæ, such as the Sword of Orion, were indeed contained in our Galaxy, but other nebular objects were different, and proved to be galaxies in their own right. The most famous of them, the Great Spiral in Andromeda, is now known to be more than two million light-years away. Neither is it a mere collection of gas and dust; it is a vast system, bigger than the Galaxy in which we live.

External galaxies are almost bewilderingly numerous, and the world's largest telescope can photograph about a thousand million of them, but most of them appear only as dim, hazy specks of light. The closer systems (within 200 million light-years, say) show definite structure; the Andromeda system is a spiral, so that it resembles a Catherine-wheel, though it lies at an angle to us and the spiral effect is rather spoiled.

The galaxies contain objects of all kinds, from normal stars to giant clusters, gaseous nebulæ and even supernovæ, but they are so remote that only three can be seen without a telescope. Here, once again, northern observers are unlucky. The two closest galaxies, known as the Clouds of Magellan, lie not far from the south celestial pole, and never rise in Europe or any part of the United States. They look rather like broken-off parts of the Milky Way, and the Large Cloud is so bright that even moonlight will not hide it.

The third galaxy is, of course, the Andromeda Spiral, which is just visible without optical aid under good conditions. It is not at all spectacular, but photographs taken with powerful telescopes show that its structure is immensely complex.

Lastly, I must not omit to say something about the Milky

Way, which has been known from the dawn of human history, and is featured in legends of all countries. To the naked eye it looks like a shining band stretching across the sky, never very clear to city-dwellers, but a superb sight when seen against a really dark background.

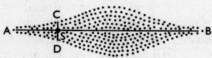

Fig. 14. The shape of the Galaxy.

When Galileo, the great Italian scientist, first turned a telescope skyward three and a half centuries ago, he saw at once that the Milky Way is made up of faint stars. The larger the telescope used, the more stars are seen, apparently almost touching each other—and yet the Milky Way is not truly crowded; once again we are dealing with a line of sight effect, due this time to the particular shape of the Galaxy.

The best way to describe the shape of the whole system is to say that it resembles two fried eggs clapped together by their backs, as shown in Fig. 14. The Sun, with its planets, lies well away from the centre, and is lettered S in the diagram. Look along the main plane of the Galaxy, toward SA or SB, and you will see large numbers of stars almost one behind the other—and this accounts for the Milky Way. Altogether, it has been estimated that the Galaxy contains a grand total of about one hundred thousand million stars. Plate V*a* shows a typical Milky Way view.

When we take an overall view of the whole scene, it is clear that to claim that "one star is like another" is not merely a gross over-simplification, but is actually wrong. There are the hot blue stars, the immense Red Giants and the dim dwarfs; there are doubles, binary stars, variables and stellar families; there are clusters, open and globular; there are the gas-and-dust nebulæ, and there are the almost frighteningly remote outer galaxies. Moreover, it is seldom nowadays that many months pass by without an important new discovery being made in some branch of astronomy. Not very long ago it was found that certain apparently star-like objects known variously as quasars, quasi-stellar objects or (for short) QSO's are intensely dramatic; they shine perhaps a million million times as brightly as the Sun, and radiate by some mechanism as yet a complete mystery to us. QSO's are the most luminous objects in the universe, and are also the most distant.

We have much to learn, and each advance raises a whole host of new problems, but at least it seems fairly certain that we have set off along the right track. Astronomy has come a long way since the days when the Greek philosophers looked up at the starlit heavens and thought, with sublime confidence, that our own puny Earth must be the centre of all things.

A NOTE ON THE STAR MAPS

The maps which follow cover the whole sky as seen from Britain and the northern United States. To select the correct monthly charts refer to the Table given on page 254.

Chapter Five

THE NORTHERN STARS

THE FIRST STEP to be taken by the would-be star-gazer is to learn his (or her) way around the sky. To identify the constellations is not nearly so difficult as it might seem, and a group which has once been found will easily be recognized again even if it contains no bright star.

Of course, much depends upon the observer's position on the surface of the Earth. As I have stressed, a set of charts designed for, say, a Londoner or a New Yorker will be of very limited use to anyone living in Sydney or Cape Town; people well south of the equator never see the Great Bear or the Pole Star, though they have ample compensation in the form of the Centaur and the Southern Cross.

In drawing up charts to be used for star recognition, the only possible method is to select one definite latitude for the observer and design the maps accordingly. In this book I have chosen 50 degrees north, which is the approximate latitude of the southernmost part of Britain and the northernmost part of the United States. In point of fact, outline maps are not badly affected by minor changes in the observer's latitude; they will do quite well for the whole of Europe and a large part of the North American continent. For all practical purposes, the charts apply to anyone observing south of Iceland and north of Mexico.

There are certain differences, of course. The bright star Fomalhaut, for instance, barely rises in North Scotland, but from Cornwall it can be quite conspicuous during autumn evenings, and in New York, Spain or Greece it reaches a considerable height above the horizon. And I well remember that when I first went to Arizona, in 1964, I was impressed by the southern part of the bright constellation Scorpio (the Scorpion), which is permanently invisible from Britain or Canada. Yet these minor alterations can be allowed for, and I have given notes about them in the chapters which follow. Only if the observer travels down to, say, Panama or Ceylon will he need a completely different set of maps.

I also gave serious thought to the question of the proper names of stars. Bayer's system of Greek letters has its drawbacks, and every constellation has its Alpha, its Beta, its Gamma and so on; but the old names are cumbersome and tongue-twisting—Dschubba, Zubenelgenubi and Azelfafage are typical examples. Since they are never used scientifically, it is better to forget about them, apart from the names of the first-magnitude stars and a few other special cases. Magnitudes, on the other hand, are important, and in general I have given them in brackets; thus Beta Aurigæ (1·9) means that the magnitude of Beta in Auriga, the Charioteer, is 1·9—fractionally brighter than the Pole Star.

So let us begin our survey of the sky as seen from latitude 50 degrees. Groups near the north celestial pole will never set, and it is fortunate that one of these constellations is the Great Bear, which is very distinctive and which makes an excellent base from which to commence operations.

URSA MAJOR: *The Great Bear*

Ursa Major is a large constellation. The so-called Plough, made up of seven stars, is only part of it, and the name itself is quite unofficial; the group has also been called King Charles' Wain, while Americans know it as the Big Dipper. On the whole, we must admit that the Americans are the more rational. The pattern is nothing like the outline of a bear or a plough, but it does give a slight impression of a spoon.

The Plough is shown in Fig. 15, together with the rest of the constellation, and the proper names of all seven stars have been given, because they will be used over and over again as pointers to other constellations. Starting at the end of the Plough-handle (or the handle of the dipper), the stars are:

Eta or Alkaid (1·9)	Gamma or Phad (2·4)
Zeta or Mizar (2·1)	Beta or Merak (2·4)
Epsilon or Alioth (1·8)	Alpha or Dubhe (1·8)
Delta or Megrez (3·3)	

The proper names are Arabic, and some of them have variations; Phad has also been called Phekda or Phecda, while Alkaid has a second name, Benetnasch.

URSA MAJOR

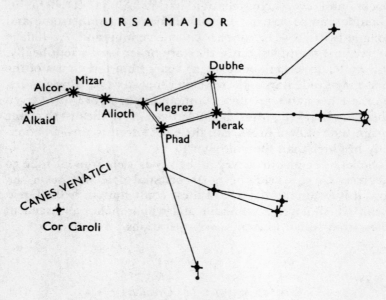

Fig. 15. Ursa Major.

The Plough is extremely easy to find, not because its stars are strikingly brilliant, but because the pattern is so well-marked. Broadly speaking, it may be seen rather low in the north during winter evenings, high in the north-east during spring evenings, high in the north-west during summer evenings, and descending in the north-west during autumn evenings. It may pass right overhead—around midnight in March, for example—and is a permanent feature of our night sky.

It may, of course, appear at all sorts of angles. Look for it during a late evening in January, and you will see the Bear "standing on its tail", as shown in Star Map 1 on page 55. But wherever it may be, it always stands out at once.

Alioth, Dubhe and Alkaid are all very slightly above the second magnitude, and to all intents and purposes we may say that they are equal, but this does not mean that their true luminosities are the same. Alkaid is 210 light-years away,

Dubhe 107 and Alioth only 68. Therefore, Alkaid is much the most powerful of the three—and the distance between it and Alioth is considerably greater than the distance between Alioth and ourselves, which is an excellent reminder that a constellation is not a separate unit.

Megrez, or Delta Ursæ Majoris, is obviously fainter than its six companions, and there is a minor mystery about it, since the old astronomers of more than a thousand years ago stated that it was as bright as the other stars of the Plough. Unless the early observers were wrong, Megrez must therefore have faded considerably, which is perfectly possible even though we can hardly be confident about it.

With one exception, all the Plough stars are white. The exception is Dubhe, which is somewhat orange in hue, showing that its surface temperature is lower. The naked-eye observer, however, will be hard pressed to see any colour at all, and the most that can normally be said is that Dubhe appears slightly "off-white". Binoculars bring out the difference quite well.

The most famous member of the Plough is Mizar, the second star in the handle (or, if you like, the second star in the Bear's tail). On any clear night a much fainter star, Alcor, may be seen close beside it, making up a naked-eye double. The old English country name for the pair was "Jack and his Wagon". The Arab astronomers of long ago certainly knew about Alcor, and have provided us with another problem which has never been completely solved.

Alcor is an easy naked-eye object. I am slightly short-sighted—that is to say, I put on spectacles when driving a car, or when playing cricket or tennis—but I have no trouble in seeing Alcor even without my distance glasses. Not long ago I asked a dozen Boy Scouts who were beginning work for their Starman's Badges to look at the Plough and see whether they could note anything unusual. All of them, quite independently, noticed Alcor even though they had not previously known about it.

Alcor is, in fact, quite conspicuous—and yet the Arabs described it as a test of naked-eye vision, hinting that it would not be seen except under really good conditions. It may have brightened up during the past thousand years or so, just as Megrez may have faded. At any rate, it still provides some sort of a test with regard to the state of the sky. Mist will conceal it, and so will moonlight. If you can make out Alcor at a glance, you may be sure that there is no haze about.

There is one more interesting fact about the Plough. Apart from Alkaid and Dubhe, its members seem to be travelling through space in much the same direction at much the same velocity, so that they make up what is termed a "moving cluster". Needless to say, the individual shifts are so slight that they are not detectable with the naked eye over many lifetimes; if it were possible to return to the days of King Canute, Julius Cæsar or Tutankhamen, the Plough would look just the same as it does now. Yet eventually the shape will change, and in, say, A.D. 50,000, the present pattern will have become very much distorted, with Alkaid lying "below" Mizar and Dubhe having made off away from its companions.

Undoubtedly the Plough is the most useful "signpost" in the sky, at least to Britons and North Americans. Not only is it so easy to find, but it is always visible. The next diagram shows it together with various other constellations to be described below; not all these are circumpolar, but the position of the Plough itself will indicate how many

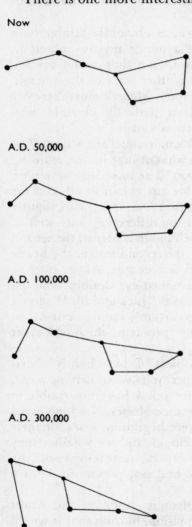

Now

A.D. 50,000

A.D. 100,000

A.D. 300,000

Fig. 16. Progressive change in the pattern of the Plough.

36

of the surrounding groups are in view and how many are not. When the Plough is standing upright over the horizon, for instance, there is no point in looking for Arcturus, which will be out of view.

The rest of Ursa Major covers a wide area, but is not particularly conspicuous. There are two triangles, made up of stars between magnitudes 3 and 4, easy to identify when the group is high in the sky, but easily obscured by horizon mist when the Plough is at its lowest.

URSA MINOR: *The Little Bear*

Once the Plough has been found, there should be no difficulty in locating Ursa Minor, the Little Bear—or, as the Americans call it, the Little Dipper. By pure coincidence, the shape of Ursa Minor is not unlike that of the Plough, though the individual stars are fainter.

The obvious way to find Ursa Minor is to use Merak and Dubhe, the two "Pointers" in the Plough, as direction-finders. An imaginary line from Merak, passing through Dubhe and prolonged for some distance, will arrive at a second-magnitude star which is none other than Polaris, leader of Ursa Minor. Polaris lies less than a degree away from the north pole of the sky, and so seems to remain almost stationary, with all the other celestial bodies moving round it once in 24 hours. Let us repeat that this distinction has nothing whatsoever to do with Polaris itself, and neither has it always marked the pole. The Earth's axis shifts very slowly in direction, and by the year A.D. 12,000 the brilliant Vega will occupy pride of place.

Because Polaris hardly moves, it is always easy to locate. If there is any doubt, note its position as compared with some natural object close at hand; for instance, stand outside your front door and see where Polaris lies compared with a nearby tree-branch. You will then be able to re-locate it when you next look.

Navigators find it very useful, because its altitude above the horizon is virtually the same as the observer's latitude on the Earth. Thus from London, where the latitude is 52 degrees, Polaris will be at an altitude of 52 degrees; from New York, latitude 40 degrees, Polaris will be only 40 degrees above the horizon (in round figures, that is to say). Centuries ago, before

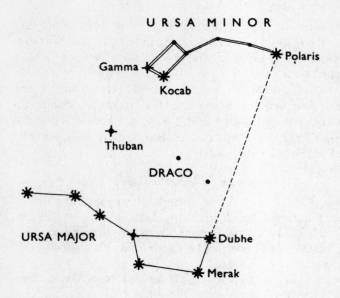

Fig. 17. Ursa Minor.

modern navigational methods had been developed, Polaris provided sailors with an excellent means of finding their latitude, though it is true that longitude-finding posed more troublesome problems. During the war, aircraft navigators used it in much the same way, measuring its altitude by means of a sextant and then applying a slight correction, known as the Q-correction, to allow for the fact that Polaris is almost a degree away from the actual pole.

In itself Polaris does not seem striking. Its magnitude is exactly 2, so that it is rather brighter than Merak, not quite so bright as Dubhe. Actually it is very luminous, and lies at a distance of 680 light-years; it is the equal of 3,000 Suns put together. It is somewhat yellowish, though I doubt whether a naked-eye observer will record it as anything but white.

The apparent distance between Polaris and Dubhe is about five times that between the Pointers, Dubhe and Merak. It is impracticable to give such distances in inches or feet, and the only possible method is to use angular measure, as illustrated in Fig. 18. Dubhe and Merak are about 5 degrees apart, so that the distance between Dubhe and Polaris is between 25 and 30 degrees.

The rest of Ursa Minor is easily located as soon as Polaris has been found. It resembles a dim and distorted Plough, stretching down in the general direction of Mizar, and ending in two stars which are bright enough to be conspicuous— Beta or Kocab (2·0) and Gamma (3·1). Kocab, sometimes nicknamed "the Guardian of the Pole", is equal to Polaris,

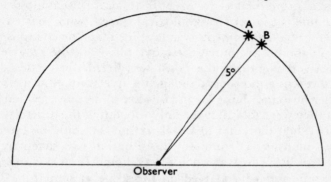

Fig. 18. Angular Distances. The distance between stars A and B is 5 degrees.

but decidedly different in colour. A careful glance will show that it is orange, though binoculars are needed to bring out the hue strongly.

The rest of the stars in the Ursa Minor pattern are fainter, so that mist or moonlight will drown them. When the sky is dark and clear, however, they are obvious enough, and in spite of its dimness the outline of the lesser Bear is unmistakable.

Both Ursa Major and Ursa Minor were included in the list of 48 constellations given by Ptolemy, the last great astronomer of ancient times, who flourished around A.D. 150. As with most of Ptolemy's groups, there is a legend attached to them. It is said that Ursa Major was once a princess named Callisto, who was so beautiful that the queen of the gods, Juno, became jealous of her and was unkind enough to turn her into a bear. (Other versions say that Jupiter, ruler of Olympus, effected the transformation in order to protect her, but the result was the same!) Later, Callisto's son Arcas came across the bear while he was out hunting, and drew his bow in readiness to shoot. Jupiter thereupon intervened, changing Arcas into a bear also and swinging both animals up into the sky, their tails being stretched in the process.

CASSIOPEIA

The third of the famous circumpolar groups, Cassiopeia, is almost as prominent as the Great Bear, and is just as interesting. The name is that of a mythological queen, who boasted that her daughter Andromeda was lovelier than the nymphs who lived in the ocean. Since these nymphs were the children of the sea-god Neptune, the boast was decidedly tactless, and Neptune sent a monster to ravage the queen's land. Cassiopeia and her husband, King Cepheus, were in despair, particularly when they were told that the only way out of the difficulty was to chain their daughter to a rock so that she could be eaten by the sea-monster. Fortunately the situation was saved by the hero Perseus, who was on his way home from a dangerous expedition and who arrived on the scene at something later than the eleventh hour. He disposed of the monster, and, in the time-honoured fashion, was awarded the princess's hand in marriage. We shall meet these various characters again later; all of them are in the sky—even the sea-monster.

Cassiopeia does not look in the least like a queen. The five chief stars of the group make up a distinct W or M, and may be found without any trouble at all. The procedure is to use two more pointers, this time Mizar and Polaris, as shown in Fig. 19. A line from Mizar through Polaris, extending for about the same distance on the far side, will lead straight to Cassiopeia, so that in effect Cassiopeia, Polaris, and the Plough-handle are in a straight line.

The stars in the W are comparable with those of the Plough, but two of them are variable, which makes them worth watching even though their fluctuations are not usually very great. The two variables are Alpha and Gamma, while the other stars in the pattern are constant—Beta at magnitude 2·3, Delta at 2·7 and Epsilon at 3·3. Note that Epsilon Cassiopeiæ is almost exactly equal to Megrez in the Great Bear.

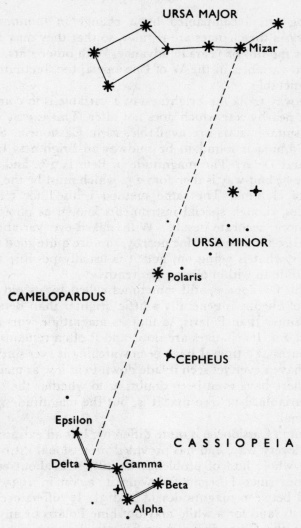

Fig. 19. Cassiopeia.

Variable stars are not uncommon, and many thousands are known, but only a few seem bright enough to be followed with the naked eye. This is not because they are genuinely faint; most of them are very luminous, but they are also extremely remote. As we have seen, a variable is a star in which the conditions are unstable, resulting in a short-term shrinking and swelling-out, accompanied by a change in luminosity. In some cases the changes are regular, so that they may be forecast for months or years in advance. With other stars, such as the two variables in the W of Cassiopeia, the fluctuations are unpredictable.

The way to fix the brightness of a variable is to compare it with a nearby star which does not alter. This is easy enough when suitable stars are available, as in Cassiopeia. Suppose that Gamma is found to be midway in brightness between Beta and Delta? The magnitude of Beta is 2·3, and that of Delta 2·7; half-way is therefore 2·5, which must be the magnitude of Gamma. The same method is used for telescopic variables, though special instruments known as photometers give more accurate results. With naked-eye variables, the comparisons made by using nearby stars are quite good enough to show what is going on, and it is usually possible to fix a magnitude to within one or two tenths.

Alpha Cassiopeiæ, still sometimes called by its old proper name of Shedir, is generally a little brighter than Beta and a little fainter than Polaris, so that its magnitude works out at around 2·2. Its changes are slow, and it often remains steady for months at a time. I have been watching it ever since 1935, and I have never yet seen it fade down to as low as magnitude 2·7. There have even been doubts as to whether the star is a true variable. I believe that it is, but the magnitude range is very small.

Gamma Cassiopeiæ is quite different; it is an extraordinary star in every way, and has provided professional astronomers with a whole host of problems. Usually it is about equal to Beta, but since I began following it, again in 1935, it has ranged between magnitudes 1½ and 3¼. It suffers occasional outbursts, and for a while may outshine Polaris or any of the stars in the Great Bear, though since the war it has been comparatively well-behaved. Since it is always capable of springing surprises on us, it makes an interesting study for the naked-eye observer.

The Milky Way passes through Cassiopeia, and anyone equipped with binoculars will find some grand star-fields available. Binoculars will also show that of the W stars, Alpha is decidedly orange, while the rest are white.

CEPHEUS

It has been said that "the female of the species is more deadly than the male". In the case of the Cassiopia legend, the female of the species is certainly more conspicuous than the male, since King Cepheus cannot be compared with his wife. In fact, Cepheus is not particularly easy to identify, since he is rather faint and has no obvious shape.

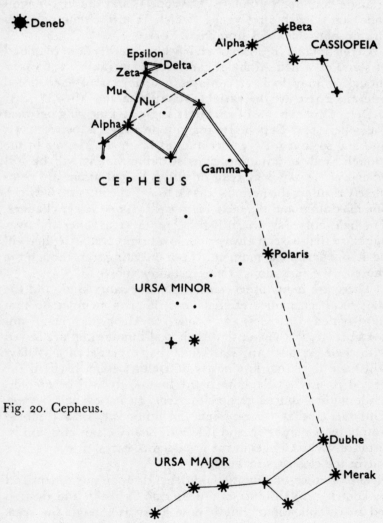

Fig. 20. Cepheus.

I have found that there are two good methods. The first is to continue the line from Merak and Dubhe, in the Plough, through Polaris; the line will reach Gamma Cephei (3·2), after which the rest of the group may be recognized. The second guide is given by Cassiopeia, since two of the W stars (Alpha and Beta) show the way to Alpha Cephei (2·4). It is also worth noting that the whole of Cepheus lies inside the triangle bounded by Polaris, Cassiopeia, and the first-magnitude star Deneb in Cygnus, which is just circumpolar in Britain but which sets from New York.

Cepheus takes the form of a fairly large, rather faint diamond of stars, of which Alpha is the leading member. Yet vague though it may look, it contains two objects of exceptional interest. These are the variable stars Delta and Mu.

Delta Cephei is one of a small triangle of stars lying between Cassiopeia and Deneb. Its magnitude range is between 3·5 and 4·4, so that it never becomes as bright as Megrez in the Plough, and at minimum it is so faint that it will be lost whenever the sky is moonlit or misty. Its variations are completely regular; the period—that is to say, the interval between one maximum and the next—is 5·37 days, and never changes. The light-curve, shown in Fig. 13, repeats itself over and over again, so that we can always tell how bright Delta Cephei will be at any particular moment. It is a pulsating star, though the cause of the pulsations is not certainly known.

There are many other variables of the same kind, and the class has been named after its most famous member, so that short-period variables are known as Cepheids. Their importance lies in the fact that their real luminosities are linked with their periods. Any star which has a period of 5·37 days will have the same luminosity as Delta Cephei itself; if the period is—say—7 days, then the luminosity will be greater, while with a shorter period the true brilliancy will be less. This means that we can find the luminosity of a Cepheid simply by watching it, and it follows that we can also find its distance. Delta Cephei lies at 1,300 light-years, but even so it is one of the closest of its kind.

The distance-finding method depends upon our starting off by knowing the distance of at least one Cepheid, and this has led to complications, but it now looks as though the scale adopted is fairly reliable. Cepheids act as our "standard candles" in space, and modern astrophysicists would be sadly lost without them. The relationship between period and luminosity is remarkably useful, even though its cause is still something of a mystery.

For Delta Cephei there are two convenient comparison stars nearby, Zeta (3·3) and Epsilon (4·2), so that anyone with a little patience can watch it from night to night and follow what it is doing.

The second variable is Mu, about mid-way between Alpha and the small triangle which includes Delta. Mu Cephei has the distinction of being the reddest star visible without a telescope; the great observer of a century and a half ago, Sir William Herschel, called it "the Garnet Star", and the nickname is an apt one. The light-changes are irregular, and Mu never becomes much brighter than the fourth magnitude, while at minimum it may be so faint that it is hard to see at all without optical aid. To one side of it lies another star, Nu (4·5) which is useful as a comparison for the variable.

Really keen-sighted people claim that they can detect the redness of Mu Cephei with the naked eye. When near maximum it certainly looks different from its companions, but the intensity of its light is too low for the colour to be conspicuous. Use binoculars, and the transformation will be immediate, as Mu then looks like a glowing coal. It is very remote; it is classed as a Red Giant, and is of the same type as the nearer and far more spectacular Red Giants such as Betelgeux in Orion.

Cepheus is so near the pole that from Britain or New York State it is always fairly high up. Though it is a relatively barren group, the presence of the two fascinating variables makes it well worth studying.

LACERTA: *The Lizard*

Adjoining Cepheus and Cassiopeia is a much smaller group, Lacerta, introduced to the sky by an astronomer named Hevelius in 1690. Hevelius, a Danzig merchant, was an energetic and skilful observer, and his star catalogue was good for its time. Altogether he drew up eleven new constellations, of which nine are still to be found on modern charts while the other two have been tacitly forgotten.

It must be said that there was little reason for making Lacerta into a separate group. One way to find it is by using the W of Cassiopeia, since Gamma and Beta point directly toward it. However, there are no stars in Lacerta brighter than the fourth magnitude, and neither are there any interesting objects. During autumn evenings it passes practically overhead.

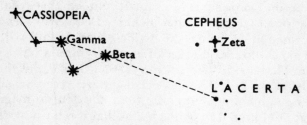

Fig. 21. Lacerta.

The one notable fact about the constellation is that two novæ have appeared in it during the present century. A nova, remember, is not a fresh star; it is simply a star which suffers a major outburst, and flares up for a few days, weeks or months before fading back to its old state. The reason for the explosion is not known in detail, but the outburst seems to affect only the star's outer layers, so that no lasting damage to the star itself is done.

In 1910 a nova was seen in Lacerta, and reached naked-eye visibility for a short time, though it soon faded. The nova of 1936 was brighter, since at maximum it more than equalled Polaris. It lay on the very edge of Lacerta, close to the triangle of stars in Cepheus. Of course, it is still visible, but nowadays large telescopes are needed to show it.

Novæ cannot be predicted, and we can never tell just when or where they will flash out, but most of them lie not far from the Milky Way—and the Milky Way band passes right through Lacerta. This is not to suggest that any more novæ may be expected there in the near future. The constellation is so small and insignificant that it has had more than its fair share of novæ for a long time to come.

DRACO: *The Dragon*

Our next constellation is the famous Dragon, which winds its way along in a line of stars not far from the Plough and Ursa Minor. Before coming to Draco, however, it will help to make a slight digression in order to introduce two particularly brilliant stars, Capella and Vega, both of which are circumpolar in Britain and practically so in New York. Capella is the leader of the important group Auriga, the Charioteer, while Vega lies in Lyra, the Lyre or Harp.

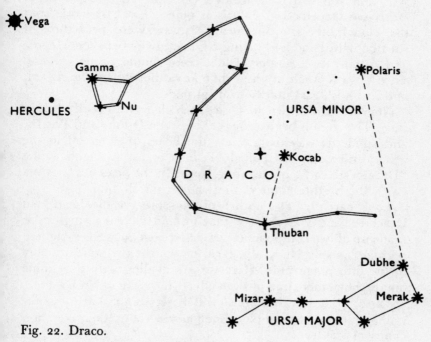

Fig. 22. Draco.

Capella and Vega are both ranked of magnitude 0·0, so that there is virtually no difference between them; of all the stars visible from Europe, only Sirius and Arcturus are brighter. It so happens that they lie on opposite sides of the Pole Star, so that when Vega is high up Capella is low down, and vice versa. During summer evenings the beautiful blue Vega is almost overhead, with Capella skirting the northern horizon; during winter evenings the position is reversed, with Capella occupying the position of eminence. If you see a bright star right above you, assuming that you are observing from Britain or the United States, then you may be quite sure that you are looking at either Capella or Vega.

In Star Map 1 on page 55, the whole area of the sky containing these two stars has been shown, which will help the beginner in finding them. Capella is probably the easier, because Megrez and Dubhe, in the Plough, show the way to it; extend the line until you come to a really brilliant yellowish star, and you will have located Capella. To identify Vega, either use Capella and Polaris as pointers, or else work from the Plough, though this means the awkward procedure of starting with Phad and taking a line midway between Megrez and Alioth. As a matter of fact there should be no trouble, since Vega is much brighter than any other star in the region, and its bluish cast marks it out at once.

Now we can return to Draco, which has no really bright stars. The stream begins roughly between Dubhe and Polaris, and winds its way in between the Bears, making off in the general direction of Cepheus. It then turns, and ends at the "Dragon's Head", not far from Vega. In the head lies Gamma (2·2), the brightest star in the whole constellation.

Look carefully at another of the stars in the head, Nu Draconis, and you will see that instead of being single it is made up of two components, very close together. Keen-sighted persons can split Nu easily, even though the two stars are only of the fifth magnitude. Here we are dealing with a genuine binary, not a mere line-of-sight effect; the twins of Nu Draconis are associated, but they are so widely separated that they take millions of years to complete one journey round their common centre of gravity.

There are few other objects in Draco likely to interest the naked-eye observer, but we should pause to say something Alpha, which lies between Mizar in the Plough and Kocab in Ursa Minor. It is only of magnitude 3·6, and so is not at all prominent, but it is celebrated because at the time when the Egyptians built their Pyramids it used to be the pole star. The celestial pole has shifted since, because of the wobbling of the Earth's axis, and Alpha Draconis has lost its distinction. It is sometimes known by its old proper name, Thuban.

In mythology, Draco was a particularly fierce dragon which was summarily and efficiently dispatched by the hero Hercules. It covers a large area, and a few minutes concentration on a clear night will enable the beginner to pick out the long, straggly line of faint stars beginning near the Pointers and ending in the "head" close to Vega.

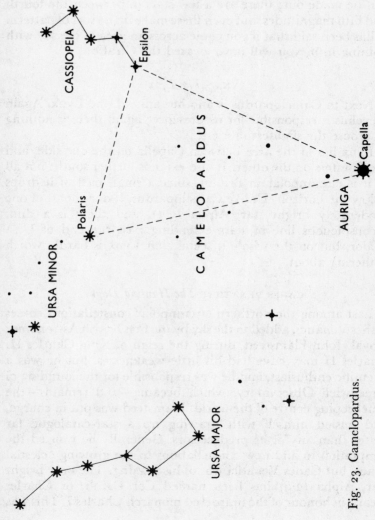

Fig. 23. Camelopardus.

CAMELOPARDUS: *The Giraffe*

Camelopardus is without doubt one of the dullest of the northern constellations. Hevelius added it to the sky in his maps of 1690, but it contains no bright stars and no objects of interest (see Fig. 23).

Broadly, Camelopardus fills the triangular area bounded by Capella, Polaris, and Epsilon Cassiopeiæ in the W. Very little can be made out; there are a few stars of between the fourth and fifth magnitudes, but even these make up no sort of pattern. It has been said that if you come across an area of the sky with nothing in it, you will have located the Giraffe!

LYNX: *The Lynx*

Next to Camelopardus is another animal, the Lynx. Again Hevelius is responsible for its presence; again there is nothing to arouse the slightest interest.

Lynx lies in the area between Capella on the one side, and the Pointers on the other. It also extends further south; not all of it is circumpolar in Britain, since a small part of it drops below the horizon. Unlike Camelopardus, it does boast of one moderately bright star, Alpha (3·2), and there is a dim, inconspicuous line of stars extending past the end of Ursa Major, but on the whole it seems that Lynx is hardly worth bothering about.

CANES VENATICI: *The Hunting Dogs*

Last among the northern circumpolar constellations comes Canes Venatici, added to the sky by the first British Astronomer Royal, John Flamsteed, during the reign of King Charles II. Charles II may have had his little weaknesses, but he was a scientific enthusiast, and he was responsible for the founding of Greenwich Observatory, which became—and remains—the timekeeping centre of the world. Flamsteed was put in charge, and busied himself with drawing up a star-catalogue far better than any of its predecessors. Generally he resisted the temptation to add new constellations to the growing celestial chaos, but Canes Venatici was of his making. The only bright star, Alpha (2·9) has been named Cor Caroli, or Charles Heart, in honour of the murdered monarch Charles I. This was

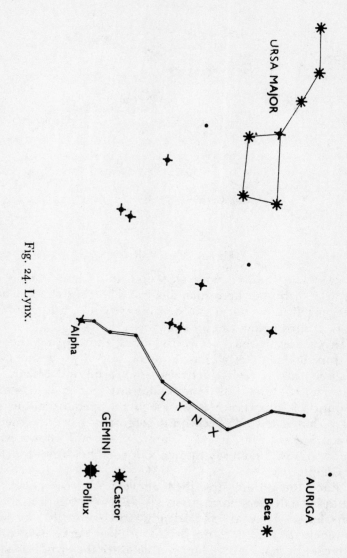

Fig. 24. Lynx.

a tactful move at the time, and the name is still used even by those who maintain that Charles deserved his fate.

Cor Caroli lies in a rather isolated position not far from the tail of the Great Bear; Dubhe and Phad point roughly toward it. There are not other stars above the fourth magnitude, and there is certainly no definite outline. Originally the maps

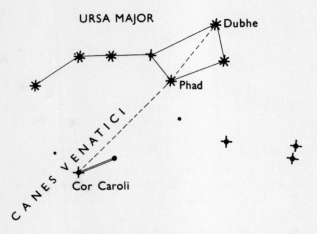

Fig. 25. Canes Venatici.

showed two hunting dogs, Asterion and Chara, being held on a leash by the herdsman Boötes. The constellation never sets over Britain, but it can become very low, and from New York it dips below the horizon.

In passing, it may be worth noting that during the 18th century Bode, a German astronomer, added yet another constellation in the region between Cor Caroli and Mizar. This was named Quadrans, the Quadrant. Since it contained nothing of importance it was soon dropped from the starmaps, but it has not been quite forgotten, since the meteors which radiate from it every January are still known as the Quadrantids. I shall say more about the Quadrantid meteors in Chapter 21.

Since the groups described above are circumpolar from latitude 50 degrees north, they will appear on all our monthly star-charts. They are old friends, and the night sky seems strangely unfamiliar to the Britain or New Yorker who travels so far south that he is no longer able to see the W of Cassiopeia or the seven stars of the Plough.

Chapter Six

THE STARS OF JANUARY

MONTHLY STAR-CHARTS are published in various journals, including a few national newspapers. Unfortunately most of them are drawn in circular form, which is perfectly accurate, but which makes the charts difficult to use. I have preferred to give two hemispherical maps for each month, one showing the northern aspect of the sky and the other showing the southern aspect. It is true that constellations near the overhead point become distorted, and this would be a serious drawback for precision charts, but it must be stressed at once that the hemispheres given here are meant to be used for recognition purposes only. Moreover, I have, I hope, avoided the common fault of putting in too many stars. What I have tried to do is to show the main patterns; once these have been identified, the rest is easy.

It should never be forgotten that these charts apply to northern countries such as Britain and New York State. Further south, the Pole Star is lower, and new groups come into view, though the differences are not very obvious until one has travelled as far as, say, Mexico or Egypt.

Each pair of charts has been drawn for 22 hours G.M.T. (= Greenwich Mean Time). Astronomically, the 24-hour clock is always used, and artificial manœuvres such as Summer Time are shunned. Therefore, 22 hours is the same as 10 p.m., or 11 p.m. when Summer Time is in operation.

One month means a difference in star-positions of approximately two hours, and so the set of charts may be adapted for any season. For instance, the aspect at 10 p.m. on January 1 will be the same as that for 8 p.m. on February 1, or 6 p.m. on March 1. In fact, all that need be done is to subtract two hours a month. Working backwards through the year, one has to add two hours a month; thus the view at midnight on December 1 will be the same as that at 10 p.m. on January 1.

An example should make this clear. The January charts given on the opposite page are for 22 hours G.M.T., or 10 p.m. The view will be the same on the following dates:

October 1	4 a.m.	(4 hours G.M.T.)
November 1	2 a.m.	(2 hours G.M.T.)
December 1	midnight	(0 hours G.M.T.)
January 1	10 p.m.	(22 hours G.M.T.)
February 1	8 p.m.	(20 hours G.M.T.)
March 1	6 p.m.	(18 hours G.M.T.)

So if you want to find out which groups are on view in the early hours of an October morning, simply look at the charts given here for January evening. The two-hour rule is not exact, but it is quite good enough for ordinary purposes.

It follows, of course, that what is usually called a "winter constellation", such as Orion, is not visible only during the winter. It is just as well seen on an autumn morning. However, most people do their sky-watching before going to bed, so that charts drawn for evening aspects are more widely useful.

THE JANUARY SKY

If you look north-east late on a January evening, the first group you will notice will certainly be the Great Bear, with its tail pointing towards the horizon. Polaris, of course, will be in its customary position, due north (it can never be anywhere else), and Cassiopeia will be high in the north-west. There should be no trouble in finding Cepheus, Draco and the other circumpolar groups, though it is true that the Dragon's head will be very low down.

At this time Capella is practically at the zenith, or overhead position. It belongs to the southern-aspect map, but I have shown it on the northern chart also so that it can act as a link between the two. But though Capella is at its best, Vega, on the opposite side of the pole, is as low down as it can ever be; it lies close to the British horizon, so that any mist or low cloud will hide it, and from New York it cannot be seen at all. Rather higher than Vega is the bright star Deneb, leader of Cygnus (the Swan).

If you use the Pointers, Dubhe and Merak in the Plough,

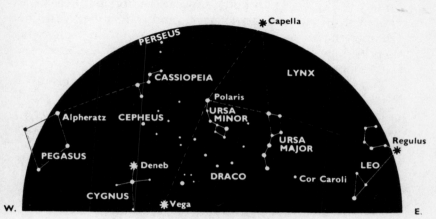

NORTHERN ASPECT

SOUTHERN ASPECT

in the reverse direction—that is to say, away from Polaris—
the line will reach the large, bright group of Leo, the Lion,
which is rising in the east and will have become a prominent
feature of the evening sky by spring. Over in the west, the
Square of Pegasus is dropping toward the horizon. Pegasus is
classed as an autumn constellation, and is described with the
October charts; for the moment, suffice to say that it may be
identified by using two of the stars in the W of Cassiopeia
as direction-finders to it.

Extending between Pegasus and the equally bright group of
Perseus is a line of bright stars marking Andromeda. In point
of fact Andromeda connects Pegasus with Perseus, but on the
whole it too is best classed with the autumn groups even
though it is still high up during early evenings in January. The
almost blank area above Ursa Major indicates the large, dim
constellations of Camelopardus and Lynx.

The southern aspect is dominated by Orion, which cannot
possibly be overlooked. Its stars are much brighter than those
of the Plough, and two of them, Betelgeux and Rigel, are well
above the first magnitude; moreover the pattern of Orion is
striking, and provides us with an excellent "anchor" for
recognizing other groups. Since all Orion's neighbours will be
discussed below, there is no point in saying much more about
them in a general description of the January sky—except that
Sirius, the glorious Dog-Star, is now at its best, and twinkles
brilliantly above the southern horizon.

Winter is certainly the best time to make naked-eye observations of the stars. Not only are the evenings dark, but the
groups on view are full of interest. Sometimes there are bright
planets to add to the scene, but planets, which move about,
cannot be shown on permanent star-charts.

ORION

Orion, the mythological hunter who boasted that he was a
match for any living creature, is the most glorious constellation
in the entire sky. The main outline is formed by seven stars,
and I propose to give their proper names as well as their
Greek letters, since they will be referred to so often in the next

few chapters. They are:

Beta	(Rigel)	magnitude 0·1
Alpha	(Betelgeux)	variable between 0·1 and 0·8
Gamma	(Bellatrix)	1·6
Epsilon	(Alnilam)	1·7
Zeta	(Alnitak)	1·8
Kappa	(Saiph)	2·1
Delta	(Mintaka)	2·2; very slightly variable.

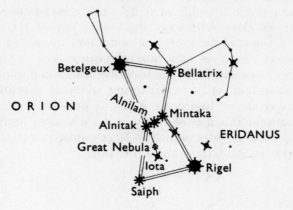

Fig. 26. Orion.

Rigel, the leader of the constellation, is a true celestial searchlight. It is so remote that its light takes 900 years to reach us, which means that we are now seeing it as it used to be at the time of the Battle of Hastings.[1] Yet even at this tremendous distance Rigel still appears as the seventh brightest star in the sky, so that obviously it must be highly luminous; the latest estimate makes it the equal of 50,000 Suns put together.

It is hard to appreciate the amount of energy being radiated by this Titanic star. Our own Sun is a mere glow-worm by comparison; were Rigel as close as, say, Mizar in the Plough it would be visible in broad daylight, and even at 900 light-years—more than five thousand million million miles—it is still striking. It is almost pure white, and when seen from

[1] Obviously this figure is not precise, but it must be of the right order. The older value of just over 500 light-years was a considerable under-estimate.

57

Britain or the northern States it usually twinkles strongly, since it is never very high up.

On page 23 something was said about the way in which a star produces its energy. The Sun is losing mass at the rate of 4 million tons every second, but Rigel, which is radiating so much more fiercely, has a mass-loss of around 80,000 million tons every second. Even a giant star of this kind cannot bear such a loss indefinitely, and Rigel will not last for long according to cosmical standards. While the Sun will look much the same in ten million years' time as it does now, Rigel will not; its glory will have departed. Yet at the present moment it is one of the most luminous stars known, squandering its energy reserves at a fantastic rate.

Betelgeux is entirely different, since any casual glance will show that instead of being glittering white, it is orange-red. Betelgeux is not so luminous as Rigel, or so remote, but to compensate for this it is of vast size. Its diameter amounts to some 250 million miles, which is large enough to contain the whole orbit of the Earth round the Sun.

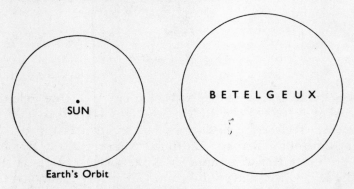

Earth's Orbit

Fig. 27. Size of Betelgeux, compared with the
Earth's orbit.

Betelgeux is a Red Giant, a term which speaks for itself. Despite its tremendous size, it is not so massive as might be thought, since its outer layers, at least, are highly rarefied. In binoculars it is a lovely sight, its rich colour showing up excellently.

Betelgeux, like so many Red Giants, is variable. It is not regular, and has little in common with the Cepheids; its fluctuations cannot be predicted with any accuracy, though there seems to be a very rough period of about five years. Sometimes it almost equals Rigel, while at others it drops down to the first magnitude and is comparable with its neighbour Aldebaran in the Bull. Betelgeux swells and shrinks, changing its output as it does so. The variations are slow, but by comparing Betelgeux with nearby bright stars the careful observer will be able to follow them.

Astronomers of thirty years ago believed Betelgeux to be a young star, not far advanced in its evolutionary cycle, so that it would gradually become smaller and hotter, developing into a white sun such as Rigel before beginning to fade into a dwarf stage. This is now known to be wrong. Betelgeux has used up most of its hydrogen "fuel", and is nearing the end of its brilliant career. Long before the Sun has shown any marked change, Betelgeux may have collapsed into a small, dense star of the kind known as a White Dwarf, though we cannot be sure; our knowledge of the life-story of a star is still limited, and the final fate of Betelgeux may be quite different.

Incidentally, the name Betelgeux is often said to mean "the Shoulder", since the star lies in the shoulder of the mythological Hunter. Alternative spellings are Betelgeuse and Betelgeuze. The name is Arabic, and its modern form seems to be the result of a series of mistranslations and misinterpretations, though originally it may well have meant "shoulder".

The other bright stars of Orion are white and hot, very similar in type to Rigel; indeed, Saiph is almost as luminous, and is even further away from us, since its distance is estimated at more than 2,000 light-years. Alnitak, Alnilam and Mintaka lie in a line, and make up the famous Belt which is so useful as a direction-marker. Mintaka or Delta Orionis, the uppermost and rather the faintest of the three, is variable over a small range (magnitude 2·2 to 2·4), but it is very doubtful whether its changes are detectable with the naked eye.

The Sword of Orion extends southwards from the Belt. It contains yet another remote, highly luminous giant, Iota (2·8), but the most remarkable feature of the Sword is the misty patch known as the Great Nebula. On a clear night the Nebula is easily visible without a telescope, and binoculars show it to be a patch of shining gas. It was first described in

1618, though since it is an obvious naked-eye object nobody can quite understand why it was not reported earlier. Later, during the eighteenth century, the French astronomer Charles Messier drew up a catalogue of more than one hundred star-clusters and nebulæ; his numbers are still used, so that the Orion Nebula is officially Messier 42 (or, for short, M.42).

The Nebula is of immense size. A ray of light would take about fifteen years to travel from one side of it to the other, so that its diameter is not much less than a hundred million million miles. It is 1,000 light-years away; the gas in it is very tenuous, and the dusty particles, too, are scattered. Inside the Nebula are various stars, of which the most celebrated is Theta Orionis—nicknamed the Trapezium because a telescope will show that it is made up of four separate suns arranged in the form of a trapezium. Theta is visible to the naked eye, but only, of course, as a single star.

Theta Orionis and the other stars mixed in with the Nebula are much hotter than the Sun, and they pour their radiation into the Nebula in all directions. This radiation affects the thin gas, and makes it shine, partly by reflection but partly because the gas itself becomes self-luminous. Other nebulæ have no convenient stars to make them visible, and so show up as dark masses, blotting out the light of stars beyond. There is no essential difference between a luminous nebula and a dark one. Unfortunately the most famous of the dark nebulæ, the so-called Coal Sack, lies in the Southern Cross, and so never rises in Europe or the United States.

The Orion Nebula is by no means the largest nebula known, but it is exceptionally close to us on the cosmical scale, since when we consider the Galaxy as a whole we must admit that a mere thousand light-years is not very much. The Hunter's Sword is both beautiful and spectacular, even though a telescope is needed to show it to best advantage.

Orion covers a wide area of the sky, and spreads out beyond the brilliant seven-star pattern. Note, for instance, the long line of fainter stars extending in a roughly north-south direction some way from Bellatrix. As a guide to other groups, Orion is unrivalled. For part of the year it is invisible, because it is too near the Sun; June, July and August skies know no Orion, and are the poorer for it, but in winter the Hunter dominates the night scene, and remains visible until disappearing into the evening twilight during springtime.

CANIS MAJOR: *The Great Dog*

During late evenings in January, the Dog-Star, Sirius, shines brilliantly in the south. Nobody can overlook it, since it is far brighter than any other star; its magnitude is −1·4, and since it never rises high in the sky it usually twinkles violently.

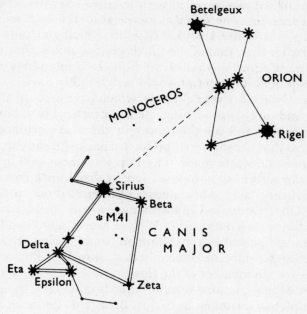

Fig. 28. Canis Major.

Sirius is the leader of Canis Major (the Great Dog). It lies in a direct line with the three stars of Orion's Belt, as shown in Fig. 28, but no pointers to it are really necessary. Yet oddly enough, Sirius is not exceptionally luminous; it is 26 times as powerful as the Sun, but it is a glow-worm compared with Rigel. Its apparent brilliance is due to the fact that it is one of the closest of all the stars. Light takes only 8½ years to reach us from Sirius, corresponding to a distance of something like 50 million million miles.

Sirius is pure white, but when low above the horizon it is seen shining through a comparatively thick layer of atmosphere, so that it flashes in all sorts of colours, ranging from red to green and blue. This has nothing to do with Sirius itself, but is an effect produced solely by the unsteadiness of the Earth's air. Through binoculars or a telescope, the many-hued flashing of Sirius is a lovely sight.

Sirus is known to be attended by a faint companion, known popularly but unofficially as "the Pup". Since it is not visible with the naked eye, or even with average-sized telescopes, it hardly concerns us here, but it merits at least a brief mention. The Pup is a White Dwarf star, with a diameter only three times greater than that of the Earth (24,000 miles), but with a mass almost equal to that of the Sun. It is incredibly dense, and a cupful of its material would weigh many tons.

White Dwarfs are very old stars, which have used up all their "fuel" and are approaching stellar death. They have no hydrogen left, and all the atoms in them are crushed and broken, so that the shattered pieces are packed tightly together with almost no waste space. The Pup was discovered in 1863, but its extraordinary nature was not realized until more than half a century later, when studies of it carried out at Mount Wilson Observatory in California gave astronomers a series of shocks. Since then many other White Dwarfs have been found, and they are probably very common, though they are so dim that we can see only the relatively close ones. The Pup remains the best-known member of the class.

Canis Major contains several other bright stars, though all are completely outshone by Sirius. Beta (2·0) lies near Sirius; well south may be seen a triangle made up of Delta (1·8), Epsilon (1·5) and Eta (2·5), never conspicuous from Europe or the New York area, but very prominent when seen from the southern United States. These three stars are worth looking at, because they are thousands of times more luminous than the Sun. Delta and Eta, particularly, are immensely powerful, and lie over 2,000 light-years away.

There is also an interesting star-cluster in Canis Major; it was lettered 41 in Messier's catalogue, and may be found not far from Sirius and Beta. Binoculars will show it easily, and it is just visible with·the naked eye on a clear night. I always find it a difficult object, but this is only because the cluster is so low down as seen from England; from countries further south, it may be found without any trouble. There are plenty of loose clusters of this sort in the sky, but it will be better to consider them in detail when we come to the most spectacular of them all, the Seven Sisters in the Bull.

The Milky Way runs through a part of Canis Major, but misses Sirius by a fair margin. All the same, the constellation is a splendid one, and would be of major importance even if it were not graced by the presence of the brightest star in the heavens.

CANIS MINOR: *The Little Dog*

Canis Minor, the second of Orion's two dogs, is marked by the bright star Procyon, whose magnitude is 0·4 and which is therefore not much fainter than Rigel.

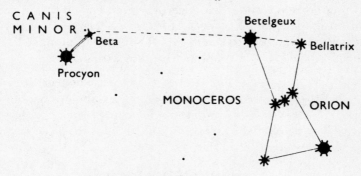

Fig. 29. Canis Minor.

The best way to find it is to use Bellatrix and Betelgeux, in Orion, as pointers. Extend a line from one to the other, and continue it for some distance, curving it slightly as shown in Fig. 29. Procyon will be found at once, partly because it is so bright and partly because there are no comparable stars anywhere near it. On January evenings it is high up, and is visible for most of the night, since it does not set until about six o'clock in the morning.

Like Sirius, Procyon is one of our nearer neighbours. It is 11 light-years away, and five times as luminous as the Sun. It is yellowish, but to the naked eye it looks white, since the yellow cast is too slight to be noticed. Like Sirius, too, it has a faint companion which is only visible with large telescopes, and which may be another of the strange, super-dense White Dwarfs.

Some distance from Procyon, rather north of a line extended to Betelgeux, is Beta (2·9), the only other notable star in Canis Minor. Beta is white-hot, and is actually much more luminous than Procyon, but it is also much further away.

MONOCEROS: *The Unicorn*

Orion and his dogs are ancient groups, but in this area there is also a modern constellation, Monoceros. "Modern" is perhaps a misleading term, since the group was added to the sky by Hevelius in 1690, but the original constellations are well over two thousand years old.

The mythological unicorn was a horned horse, but there is nothing horselike about Monoceros, which has no bright stars and no shape at all. However, it is easy to locate. Find Betelgeux, Procyon and Sirius, and link them with imaginary lines; the large triangle so formed will contain Monoceros.

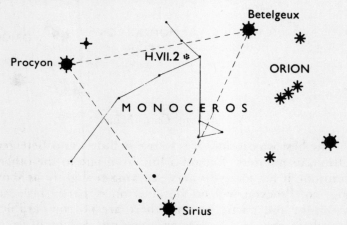

Fig. 30. Monoceros.

In point of fact Monoceros is not nearly so dull as might be thought. The Milky Way flows through it, and the whole region is very rich in faint stars even though there are no bright ones. Also, there are various clusters, of which one—

roughly between Procyon and Betelgeux—is just visible without a telescope if its position is known. It was not listed by Messier, and is known officially as H.VII.2, or the second object in a later catalogue drawn up by Sir William Herschel. It is not easy to identify, because there are so many other faint objects near it, and it is not of much interest to the naked-eye watcher.

ARGO NAVIS: *The Ship Argo*

One of the most intriguing of the ancient legends tells how a band of heroes, headed by Jason of Iolcos, sailed off in quest of the Golden Fleece. This fleece had come from a magic ram, which had been able to fly, and which had rescued two royal children from a cruel stepmother, carrying them to the land of a monarch named Æetes. After the ram died, its golden fleece was placed in a tree in a sacred grove, guarded by a particularly unpleasant dragon. Jason managed to kill the dragon, much to the annoyance of King Æetes, and took the golden fleece back to his own country.

Among the heroes concerned in the expedition were Hercules, the strongest of men, and the "heavenly twins" Castor and Pollux. The ship in which they sailed was called the Argo, and, fittingly enough, Argo Navis used to be the largest constellation in the sky. I say "used to be" because astronomers found that the original Argo was unwieldy, and it was summarily split up into three main parts, Carina (the Keel), Puppis (the Poop), and Vela (the Sails).

Most of Argo is invisible in Europe and the northern United States. This is a pity, since Carina, in particular, is very brilliant; it contains Canopus, a glorious yellow star which is outshone only by Sirius. However, part of Puppis does rise above the horizon in northern lands. Rho (2·8) may be seen some way east of the triangle formed by Delta, Epsilon and Eta Canis Majoris, with Xi (3·5) nearby. New Yorkers, though not Londoners, can catch sight of Zeta (2·2), which is an exceptionally remote star of tremendous luminosity. It may be found by using Delta and Eta Canis Majoris as pointers, but nobody who lives north of latitude 50°N. will be able to see it. The Milky Way flows through Puppis, and continues down over the southern horizon.

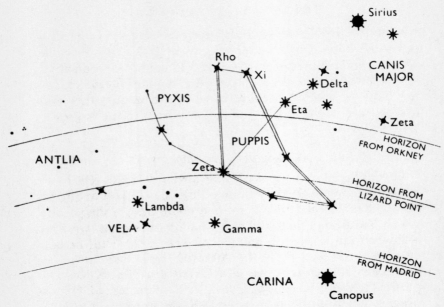

Fig. 31. Puppis. The limits of visibility for Orkney, Lizard Point and Madrid are shown.

PYXIS: *The Compass* and ANTLIA: *The Air-pump*

Puppis is at its best around 11 p.m. in early January, but it is always very low, and much of it is too far south to be seen from Europe. Adjoining it to the east are two utterly insignificant constellations, Pyxis and Antlia. Since neither contains anything of interest, and there are no stars brighter than the fourth magnitude, it seems rather pointless to draw separate maps for them, and I have simply indicated their positions on the chart drawn for Puppis. Both were added to the sky by the French astronomer Lacaille in his map of 1752, but for no apparent reason. From Britain, at least, it is doubtful whether any of the stars of Antlia will be visible with the naked eye; they are too faint and too low-down. I have looked for them on more than one occasion, but with no success.

GEMINI: *The Twins*

From these dim, elusive groups we turn next to a really brilliant constellation—Gemini, the Twins.

The two leading stars, Castor and Pollux, have been named

66

in honour of Jason's companions in the Argo. They are only 4½ degrees of arc apart, so that they are slightly closer together than the Pointers in the Great Bear. To find them, extend a line from Rigel through Betelgeux, and extend it for roughly double the distance across Orion. This is an easy method, but the Twins lie north of Orion in the sky, and are often visible when Orion is not; by six o'clock on a January morning, for instance, the Hunter has set, but the Twins are still on view. Luckily, Castor and Pollux may also be found by using our other main "anchor", the Plough. The direction-finders in this case are Megrez and Merak; the region between Merak and the Twins is occupied by the outer parts of Ursa Major and the faint, dull Lynx, so that the direction line will pass near no bright stars until it reaches Castor and Pollux.

Pollux is the brighter of the two; its magnitude is 1·2, as against 1·6 for Castor, so that the difference is quite noticeable. Moreover, Pollux is decidedly orange, whereas Castor is white. Though the Twins seem to be neighbours, they are not really close together; Castor is 45 light-years away from us, Pollux only 35.

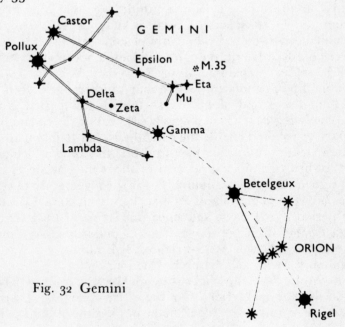

Fig. 32 Gemini

There is another minor mystery here. Ptolemy, in the 2nd century A.D., stated quite definitely that Castor was brighter than Pollux, and this was also the opinion of the Arab astronomers who charted the sky several hundreds of years later. The reverse is true to-day, so that if the old observers were correct we must suppose that either Castor has faded, or else Pollux has brightened up. It seems rather more likely that the change has occurred in Pollux.

Castor looks like a single star, but telescopes show that it is nothing of the sort. It is a binary; the two components, so close together that to the naked eye they appear as one, move round their common centre of gravity in a period of 380 years. Each component is again double, while travelling round the whole quartet is a pair of dim Red Dwarf stars. Altogether, then, Castor is made up of six suns, four bright and two faint. Stellar families are not uncommon in the Galaxy, but Castor is a particularly good example.

The rest of Gemini is made up of long streams of stars, stretching from the Twins in the general direction of Orion. Gamma, between Betelgeux on the one side and Castor and Pollux on the other, is of magnitude 1·9, which is bright enough to be conspicuous. Near it may be seen two less prominent stars, both of which are of some interest. Mu (2·9) is a remote Red Giant, though its colour is not obvious to the naked eye. Its companion, also a Red Giant, is a well-known variable, Eta Geminorum, with a magnitude range of from $3\frac{1}{4}$ to $4\frac{1}{4}$, and a period of 231 days—though this period is not completely regular. The changes are slow, but the chart given on page 234 should enable the careful watcher to follow them.

Zeta Geminorum is another variable, this time a Cepheid. It is not brilliant, since it never rises above magnitude $3\frac{3}{4}$ and drops down to $4\frac{1}{4}$ at minimum, but it is conveniently placed; it lies between Gamma and Pollux, slightly closer to Gamma. The period is $10\frac{1}{4}$ days, and since this is longer than that of Delta Cephei itself ($5\frac{1}{3}$ days), Zeta Geminorum is the more luminous of the two. At its brightest it is almost equal to its neighbours, Delta and Lambda Geminorum.

The Milky Way runs right through Gemini, and the whole region is extremely rich. On dark, clear nights, a keen-sighted person may be able to make out a dim speck near Eta which is, in fact, the lovely open cluster Messier 35. Binoculars will show it well.

AURIGA: *The Charioteer*

On a January evening, the overhead position is occupied by Capella, which is of zero magnitude and is one of the half-dozen brightest stars in the sky. It is the leader of Auriga, the celestial charioteer, who is said to have invented the four-horse chariot and to have been placed in the heavens as a fitting reward.

There is no mistaking Capella. It may be found by using the Great Bear, as described on page 48, and we can also use Orion, since a line drawn from Mintaka through Bellatrix will pass near Capella. In any case, the star's outstanding brillance marks it out at once.

Capella is obviously yellow. Its surface temperature is the same as that of the Sun (6,000 degrees Centigrade), but whereas the Sun is officially ranked as a Yellow Dwarf, Capella is a Yellow Giant; it is the equal of 200 Suns, and lies at a distance of 45 light-years. Actually it is made up of two components, and is a close binary system, but large telescopes are needed to show the two stars separately. Capella is circumpolar in Britain, though on summer evenings it almost touches the northern horizon. From New York, it disappears from view for a short time every twenty-four hours.

As we have seen, Capella and Vega lie on opposite sides of the Pole, and at almost equal distances from it, so that when Capella is high up then Vega is low down. Since the two are of almost equal brightness—Vega 0·04, Capella 0·05—a useful experiment may be carried out. On a winter evening Capella will look much the more brilliant of the two, since it is higher up, so is shining through a thinner layer of the Earth's atmosphere; Vega, not far above the skyline, will be correspondingly dimmed. This dimming, known technically as "extinction", amounts to three magnitudes for a star only one degree above the horizon; at an altitude of 10 degrees only one magnitude is lost, and at 20 degrees the extinction is reduced to half a magnitude. Above 40 degrees, the effect may be neglected. Extinction must always be taken into account when comparing two stars at different altitudes, as must often

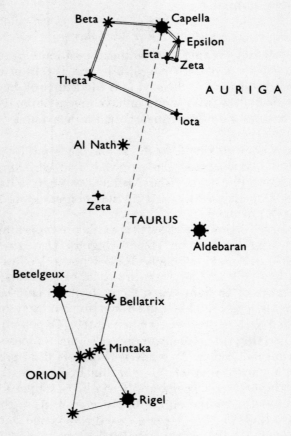

Fig. 33. Auriga.

be done when checking naked-eye variables.

Rigel, ranked as magnitude 0·08, is almost equal to Capella, but from Britain it always looks much fainter, since it is lower down. Also it will generally twinkle strongly, whereas Capella shines with comparative steadiness when it is near the overhead point.

Auriga contains several bright stars in addition to Capella; Beta (1·9) and Theta and Iota (each 2·6) complete a sort of kite-shape. There is also a bright white star of magnitude 1·6, with a proper name of Al Nath, lying between Betelgeux and

Capella. It used to be included in the Charioteer, as Gamma
Aurigæ, but for some reason it has been given a free transfer to
the neighbouring constellation of the Bull, and is now known
as Beta Tauri. There are grounds for suggesting that it would
have been better left with Auriga, since it seems to fit well into
the kite-pattern, whereas Taurus has no definite outline at all.

Next to Capella may be seen a triangle of comparatively
faint stars, nicknamed the Hædi or Kids. They seem unspectacular, but two of them are remarkable objects. Epsilon
Aurigæ, at the apex of the triangle, is only of the third
magnitude, but proves to be a binary of unusual type. The
brighter component is an extremely luminous supergiant 60,000
times as powerful as the Sun, while the dimmer member of
the pair is the largest star known, with a diameter of 1,800,000,000
miles. This "giant of giants" could swallow up much of the
Solar System, but it has only 18 times the mass of the Sun,
since the gas which makes it up is excessively thin. Nobody
has actually seen it, though it betrays its presence by its effects
upon the brighter component. Its surface temperature is a
mere 1,200 degrees, which is cool by stellar standards.

The components move round their common centre of gravity
in a period of 27 years. When the brighter star passes behind
the fainter, part of its light is blocked out, and Epsilon Aurigæ
appears to fade; it behaves like a variable, though in this case
there is no genuine change in the output of light. I shall have
more to say about these "fake" variables on page 73.

The dimmest member of the triangle, Zeta, is of the same
kind, though here the magnitude range is very small. It is
pure coincidence that these two huge star-systems should lie
side by side in the sky; there is no real link between them, and
they simply happen to be in much the same direction as seen
from Earth.

Not all of Auriga is circumpolar from Britain. Most of the
constellation sets, though Capella does not. The Milky Way
flows through it, so that it is extremely rich in faint stars.

PERSEUS

Perseus, the gallant hero of the legend about the princess
and the sea-monster, adjoins Auriga. It contains no first-
magnitude stars, but it is of great interest, and it also is

involved in the Milky Way.

Perseus may be said to belong to both the winter and autumn charts. It must be described here, because it is high up on January evenings, but in many ways it is more closely associated with Andromeda and Pegasus. From it, the line of stars marking Andromeda extends toward the western horizon, and the Square of Pegasus is also on view, though to all intents and purposes it has disappeared by midnight. I have had to leave Andromeda and Pegasus until the October sky-map, but they are very prominent during the earlier parts of January evenings.

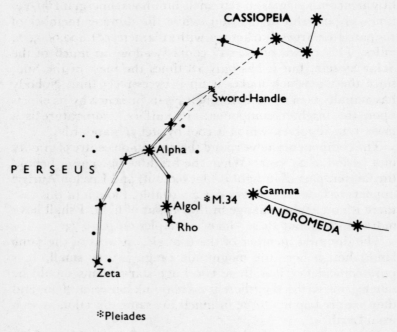

Fig. 34. Perseus.

So far as Perseus is concerned, the best pointer is Cassiopeia, since two of the W stars—Gamma and Delta—show the way to it. The Plough is too far off to be used conveniently, and neither are there any obvious guides from Orion, but on a clear night there should be no trouble; simply trace the path of the Milky Way from Capella toward Cassiopeia, and you arc bound to find Perseus. The group has a shape which is easy to recognize but rather difficult to describe. The map ought to show what is meant.

Alpha (1·8) is conspicuous, but of no special interest. The most famous star in the constellation is Beta or Algol, nicknamed the Winking Demon.

Algol looks ordinary enough, and generally looks like a second-magnitude star, but every 2 days 13 hours it starts to fade, dimming steadily for 3½ hours until it is reduced to below magnitude 3. It remains in this state for twenty minutes, after which it starts to brighten once more, taking another 3½ hours to regain its lost lustre. After that, nothing more happens for a further 2 days 13 hours, when the long, slow "wink" begins again.

Algol behaves, in fact, like a rather odd sort of variable star. The Italian astronomer Montanari noticed its fluctuations as long ago as the year 1669, but it was not until more than a century later that their cause was found. The man responsible was one of the most unusual astronomers of all time. His name

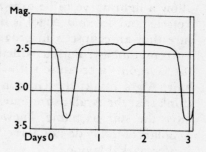

Fig. 35. Light-curve of Algol.

was John Goodricke; he was deaf and dumb, and died when aged only twenty-one, but he had shown promise of true greatness.

Goodricke realized that Algol is not one star, but two, moving round each other and forming a close binary system. One component is brighter than the other; therefore, when the brighter star is hidden by the fainter, the total light which

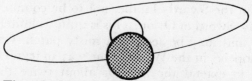

Fig. 36. The Algol pair, with the larger, fainter component concealing as much of the brighter star as it ever can—so producing the chief minimum (mag. 3·3).

we receive is reduced. Algol is best described as an eclipsing binary rather than a variable.

Modern research has shown that Goodricke was quite right. As seen from Earth the eclipse of the brighter star is not total, and there is a very slight secondary minimum when the fainter component is eclipsed, but this drop in brilliance is too slight to be noticed with the naked eye. Many other Algol-type stars are now known, though very few are visible without a telescope.

The minima of Algol can be predicted well in advance, and are listed in annual publications such as the *Handbook* of the British Astronomical Association. When a "wink" is due, observations carried out at, say, ten-minute intervals will allow a light-curve to be drawn up. If you happen to look at Perseus and see that Algol is unexpectedly faint, you may be sure that an eclipse is in progress.

In mythology, Perseus killed the terrible monster Medusa, the Gorgon—a creature with the head of a woman but snaky hair. Algol marks the Gorgon's head, and it was natural to think that the Arab astronomers of a thousand years ago, who gave the star its name, knew about its peculiar behaviour. Scholars of today do not agree, but in any case the coincidence is a remarkable one.

Next to Algol in the sky, but not in any way associated with it, is a genuine variable star, Rho Persei. Here we have a Red Giant of the Betelgeux type, fluctuating between magnitudes 3·2 and 3·8 in no set period. The red colour is very plain in binoculars, but I doubt whether it is detectable with the naked eye; the intensity of the star's light is too low.

Forming a triangle with Algol and Rho is an open star-cluster, Messier 34, which is just visible without optical aid under good conditions. However, a more spectacular object is the cluster in the Sword-Handle, not to be confused with the nebula in the Sword of Orion. This is quite definitely a naked-eye object, and may be seen as a misty patch. Gamma and Delta Cassiopeiæ, in the W, show the way to it; all that has to be done is to extend the line for about twice the distance between Gamma and Delta, as shown in Fig. 34. The Sword-Handle consists of two clusters close together, and forms a lovely telescopic object, though to the naked-eye nothing is visible except a dim blur.

The Milky Way is particularly bright in Perseus, and
of the constellation is covered. Note, too, the end star
main pattern, Zeta (2·8). It looks commonplace enoug
it is in fact a highly luminous supergiant more than a thousand
light-years away from us.

TAURUS: *The Bull*

Taurus is another splendid winter constellation. Here again
there is no difficulty in finding it whenever Orion can be seen,
since the Belt stars point upward to Aldebaran, leader of
Taurus. Aldebaran is of the first magnitude—more accurately,
0·9—and it is strongly orange-red, so that it looks like a
slightly less brilliant edition of Betelgeux.

Aldebaran is apparently contained in a scattered cluster of
stars known as the Hyades. Several members of the cluster
are visible, extending from Aldebaran in a sort of V-shape;
most of them are of between the third and fourth magnitudes,
while one, Theta, is a double wide enough to be split by
anyone with average eyesight.

I have said that Aldebaran is "apparently contained" in
the Hyades. I used the word "apparently" because Aldebaran
is not a true member of the cluster at all; it is seen in the fore-
ground, so to speak, and is 68 light-years away from us, while
the Hyades themselves are twice as remote. Aldebaran is as
far from the Hyades as we are from Aldebaran, which is hard
to believe at first sight.

This may be the moment to say a little more about open
clusters in general. The stars, as we have seen, are widely
scattered in space, and the Sun's nearest stellar neighbour is
more than twenty million million miles away even though we
live in a moderately crowded part of the Galaxy. Sometimes
true groups occur, and these make up the open clusters; the
individual stars are moving through space in the same direction
at about the same velocity, and seem to have had a common
origin. The distances between them are much less than in
average areas, though even in a dense cluster the stars are still
thousands of millions of miles apart, and there is no fear of
direct collisions. Eventually, over immense spans of time, the
gravitational pulls of non-cluster stars, together with the over-

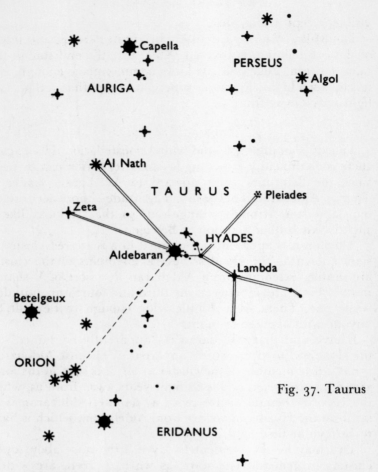

Fig. 37. Taurus

all gravitational field of the Galaxy, must scatter the cluster, though the process is a very gradual one.

The Hyades are too widely separated to be really imposing, but this is not true of the Pleiades or Seven Sisters, which also belong to Taurus. To find the cluster, continue the line from Orion's Belt through Aldebaran, and curve it slightly, as shown in Fig. 37. The Pleiades will catch the observer's attention at once; at first glance they look like a glowing patch, but a closer look will reveal several stars, of which one—Eta Tauri, or Alcyone—is of the third magnitude.

Alcyone is the brightest of the Pleiads, but Electra, Atlas,

Merope, Maia and Taygete are also visible on a clear night. Several other members of the cluster, such as Celæno and Pleione, are on the limit of naked-eye visibility. Binoculars will show more, and the total number of cluster-stars is in the region of 250. The Pleiades give the impression of being compact, but in fact the system covers an area 15 light-years in diameter. The distance from Earth is some 500 light-years.

All the leading stars of the Pleiades are hot white giants, and some of them are of special interest to professional astronomers. So far as the naked-eye observer is concerned, the main question is—How many stars can be seen? The nickname "Seven Sisters" seems to give the answer, but there have been suggestions that only six stars are usually visible. A recent

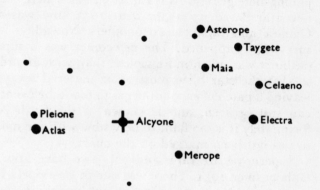

Fig. 38. The Pleiades. This chart includes stars down to magnitude 6, but few people will be able to see more than Alcyone, Electra, Atlas, Merope, Maia, Taygete and Celæno without optical aid. North is to the top.

investigation of my own indicates that this is wrong. In 1962 I presented a television programme about the Pleiades in my monthly BBC series, *The Sky at Night*, and I invited viewers to look at the Pleiades under favourable conditions, noting the number of stars seen. The results were interesting. Hundreds of replies were received, and most of them showed seven stars. A few keen-eyed people recorded eight, nine, or even (in one

77

case) eleven, but the average worked out at seven, so that the nickname is appropriate after all.

Moonlight will hide all the Pleiades except Alcyone, and even Alcyone vanishes when the Moon is near full and in that part of the sky. Mist will also conceal the group. Yet against a dark background the Pleiades are quite unmistakable, and make up by far the most conspicuous of the open clusters.

Two other features of Taurus are worthy of mention. Lambda, not far from the Hyades, is an eclipsing binary of the Algol type; it changes between magnitudes 3·3 and 4·2 in a period of just under four days, and is the brightest eclipsing star in the sky apart from Algol itself (discounting those stars whose changes are too slight to be noticed with the naked eye). A chart for it is given on page 240.

Then, too, there is Zeta Tauri (3·1), which lies on a line joining Betelgeux to Al Nath. It was near here that a brilliant new star flared up in the year 1054, and was recorded by Chinese and Japanese astronomers. Nowadays we are quite sure what happened. The newcomer was a supernova; the outburst was much more violent than with an ordinary nova, so that the star blew most of its material away into space, leaving a patch of expanding gas to mark the event. This patch can still be seen, and is known as the Crab Nebula. Unfortunately it is too faint to be visible with the naked eye, and so has not been marked on the chart.

Supernovæ are rare, and only two have appeared in our Galaxy since 1054. There was one in Cassiopeia in 1572, and another in Ophiuchus (the Serpent-bearer) in 1604. Astronomers would welcome another, but we have no guarantee whether they will be lucky in the foreseeable future. Incidentally, supernova wrecks are strong emitters of radio waves.

Taurus is a large constellation, but has no obvious shape. Apart from Aldebaran its stars are not bright, but the presence in it of the two famous clusters, the eclipsing binary Lambda, and the Crab Nebula cannot fail to make it particularly worth studying.

ERIDANUS: *The River*

Much less conspicuous is Eridanus, a long, sprawling constellation identified with the Italian river Po. According to mythology, the reckless youth Phæthon was given permission to drive the chariot of the Sun for one day, but he was unable to control the winged horses as they raced across the sky; in order to prevent the world from being set on fire, Jupiter struck him with a thunderbolt and toppled him to his death in the river.

Be that as it may, there is nothing at all distinctive about that part of Eridanus visible from Europe or North America. The brightest part of the group, including the first-magnitude star Achernar, lies in the far south, and so can never be seen. Yet Eridanus covers a wide area; during January evenings it lies in the south, with another large, dim constellation (Cetus) to one side and Orion to the other.

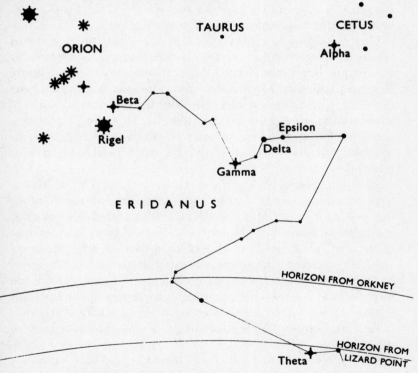

Fig. 39. Eridanus. Theta Eridani (2·9) is just invisible from England, but rises in New York. However, the brilliant Achernar (0·5) is much too far south to be seen from anywhere in the United States and so is not shown on the chart.

The leading star is Beta (2·8), which is so close to Rigel that it seems to belong more properly to the Orion pattern. Slightly fainter is Gamma (3·0), well to the west and rather lower down; it is not particularly easy to identify, since there are no obvious pointers to it, but in any case it is entirely unremarkable. However, its neighbour Epsilon (3·8) has been the subject of much attention in recent years. Epsilon forms a pair with a slightly brighter star, Delta (3·7).

Epsilon Eridani is one of the closest stars known. It is 11 light-years away from us, so that it is more remote than Sirius, but still almost on our doorstep by cosmical standards. It is cooler than the Sun, and is decidedly orange, though the colour is not strong enough to be noticed with the naked eye. For once we are dealing with a real dwarf, since Epsilon has only one-third of the Sun's luminosity.

Our own Sun is a very ordinary star, and since it has a family of planets going round it there seems no reason to doubt that other suns have planets of their own. If so, many of those planets may be inhabited by races far more intelligent than those of Earth (which, considering the present state of world affairs, would not be too difficult). However, a planet is a relatively small body, shining by reflected light, and no attendant of another star would be visible with our present telescopes.

In 1960, a team of American scientists headed by F. Drake began a somewhat peculiar investigation. They started "listening out" for possible radio signals from far-away planets, using the sensitive radio telescope at Green Bank in Virginia. Since Epsilon Eridani is one of only two nearby stars resembling the Sun, Drake concentrated upon it; if it really did happen to be accompanied by an inhabited planet, and if the hypothetical "other men" were being kind enough to transmit signals, there might be a chance of an amazing discovery. Therefore, Epsilon Eridani came in for a generous share of attention.

The whole scheme, officially termed Project Ozma but unofficially known as Project Little Green Men, caused tremendous interest, but it is very doubtful whether any of the research team had much faith in it. After a while the experiment was discontinued, but it may be started again one day. Whether Epsilon Eridani is the centre of a planetary system is still not known, and there is no immediate prospect of our finding out.

The long, straggly line of stars marking Eridanus may be traced down to the southern horizon, and is well placed during January, but on the whole this is a very barren area of the sky.

LEPUS: *The Hare*

Orion is said to have been particularly fond of hunting hares, and the little constellation of Lepus lies close to him in the sky. It has no bright stars, but Alpha (2·5) and Beta (2·8) are reasonably prominent, and there are several more between magnitudes 3 and 4 (see Fig. 40).

Lepus may be found directly below Orion; the distance between Rigel and Alpha Leporis is about the same as that between Rigel and the Hunter's Belt. There is no well-marked pattern, and neither are there any objects of note. As seen from Europe and North America, Lepus is always rather low down.

COLUMBA: *The Dove*

Still lower down, below Lepus, may be seen a few stars of another little constellation, Columba. Its leaders, Alpha (2·6) and Beta (3·1) would be easy to locate were they better placed, but they are always so near the horizon in Britain that they are hard to see, though from the latitude of New York they can be made out during January evenings when there is no mist about. In the diagram in Fig. 40, the horizon lines for London and New York are given. A line drawn from Alnitak in Orion's Belt, passed through Saiph and carried on for some distance, will arrive at the line of stars which marks Columba.

CÆLUM: *The Sculptor's Tools*

There are no remarkable objects in Columba, and the adjacent group, formerly known as Cæla Sculptoris but now shortened to Cælum, is even more obscure. It contains no star as bright as the fourth magnitude, and is always extremely low in Britain and the United States. I have often looked for

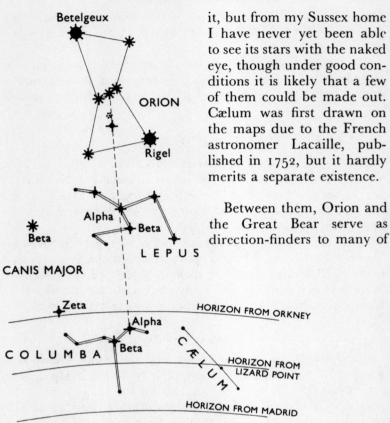

it, but from my Sussex home I have never yet been able to see its stars with the naked eye, though under good conditions it is likely that a few of them could be made out. Cælum was first drawn on the maps due to the French astronomer Lacaille, published in 1752, but it hardly merits a separate existence.

Between them, Orion and the Great Bear serve as direction-finders to many of

Fig. 40. Lepus, Columba and Cælum.

the constellations visible from our latitudes, which is an extra reason why winter is an ideal time to start learning the various groups. Perhaps I may be allowed to comment on my own method, which I started to put into practice when I was about seven years old. Armed with a set of ancient star-maps, I made a pious resolution to identify one new constellation every night. I found that a few minutes' observation on each clear evening proved quite adequate, and it was not long before I could recognize most of the groups at a glance. Star recognition is not, in fact, at all difficult for anyone who has a little patience.

Chapter Seven

THE STARS OF FEBRUARY

THE TWO-HOUR difference between the 10 p.m. charts for January and February results in a considerable shift. Orion will be found to have moved well over toward the west, though still excellently placed, while Capella will be somewhat west of the overhead point.

The maps given here apply to the following times:

October 1	6 a.m.	(6 hours G.M.T.)
November 1	4 a.m.	(4 hours G.M.T.)
December 1	2 a.m.	(2 hours G.M.T.)
January 1	midnight	(0 hours G.M.T.)
February 1	10 p.m.	(22 hours G.M.T.)
March 1	8 p.m.	(20 hours G.M.T.)

It also applies to April 1 at 6 p.m., and so on, though at six o'clock on an April evening the sky is still too light for any stars to be seen.

Taking the northern aspect first, the Great Bear is to be found high up in the north-east, still with its tail pointing in the general direction of the horizon. Follow round the curve of the tail, and you will come to an extremely bright orange star; this is Arcturus in Boötes (the Herdsman), still low down, but becoming conspicuous by the early hours of the morning. Vega is at its very lowest. Its position can be checked by using Capella and Polaris—remember that Polaris lies almost exactly half-way between Capella and Vega—and from Britain it can usually be found, though from New York it is briefly out of view. Deneb in Cygnus is little higher, and since it is not nearly so brilliant as Vega it may well be overlooked.

The ever-present Cassiopeia rides high in the north-west, and other circumpolar groups such as Ursa Minor, Draco and Cepheus are also on view. So is Perseus, which is not conveniently shown on the hemispherical charts because it spreads

83

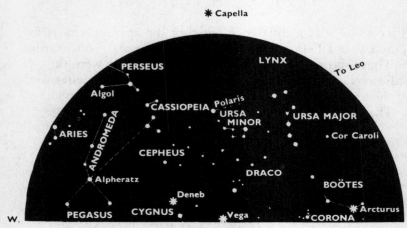

NORTHERN ASPECT

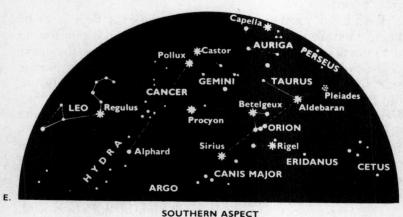

SOUTHERN ASPECT

from one on to the other. The Square of Pegasus is setting, and is hardly likely to be seen.

The southern aspect is still ruled by Orion. Eridanus has become low, but Sirius is at its best, and this is also a good time to look for the visible part of Argo. Aldebaran is starting to descend in the west, and will set by 3 a.m., following the Pleiades cluster below the horizon.

To compensate for this, the spring groups are arriving on the scene. It seems best to leave a description of them until the April chart, but it must be said at once that nobody who looks intelligently at the sky can fail to notice the grand constellation of Leo, the Lion, with its first-magnitude star Regulus. A large part of the south-east is occupied by Hydra, the Watersnake, which has the distinction of being the largest of all constellations (excluding the now-dismembered Argo) and is also one of the dullest.

One notable feature of the sky during February evenings is the Milky Way, which runs from the northern horizon to the southern, passing through Cassiopeia, Perseus, Auriga, Gemini, Monoceros, and past Sirius into Argo before being lost to view. City-dwellers are unfortunate here, since they can never hope to see the shining belt at all clearly, but from the country, well away from sodium lamps and other undesirable features of modern civilization, the effect is magnificent. Of course, moonlight will drown it—but there are always long periods when the Moon is out of the way, to the regret of lunar observers but to the relief of those people who are anxious to see the full beauty of the stars.

Chapter Eight

THE STARS OF MARCH

ANOTHER TWO-HOUR shift brings us to the chart for 10 p.m. on March 1. The maps apply to the following times:

November 1	6 a.m.	(6 hours G.M.T.)
December 1	4 a.m.	(4 hours G.M.T.)
January 1	2 a.m.	(2 hours G.M.T.)
February 1	midnight	(0 hours G.M.T.)
March 1	10 p.m.	(22 hours G.M.T.)
April 1	8 p.m.	(20 hours G.M.T.)

A word of warning here. Let me repeat that astronomers are very scornful of artificial manœuvres such as Summer Time; civil clocks are put forward an hour to make for lighter evenings. Summer Time is never used scientifically, and neither are other times zones, such as Mountain Time and Pacific Standard Time in the U.S.A. Everything is reckoned according to Greenwich Mean Time, or G.M.T.

Since the summer-time period in Britain is altered from year to year, I have made no attempt to allow for it in this book, but remember that 20 hours G.M.T. during the time when summer rules are in operation stands for 9 p.m., not 8 p.m. as it would otherwise do.

By 10 p.m. on March 1 the Great Bear is approaching the zenith, though it still lies somewhat east of the overhead point. Arcturus, in line with the curve of the Bear's tail, is already quite high, and its great brilliance makes it stand out; it is fully the equal of Capella and Vega, though comparisons are not easy to make during March evenings, since Capella is considerably higher than Arcturus while Vega is still low in the north.

Continuing the curve of the Bear's tail through Arcturus, we come to another first-magnitude star, Spica in Virgo. The relationship is not well shown on the hemispherical charts, but the maps given in Chapter 9 should be helpful. Cassiopeia and

86

NORTHERN ASPECT

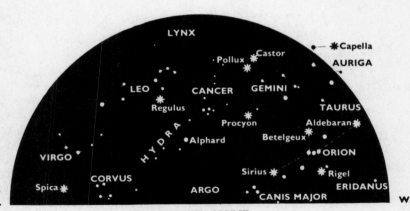

SOUTHERN ASPECT

Perseus are now in the north-west, while the Square of Pegasus has set.

Orion, together with Aldebaran and the Pleiades, is dropping toward the horizon; Sirius is low, though the Twins and Procyon remain well placed. Leo, the celestial lion, is prominent in the south; the huge area of Hydra, taking up much of the southern aspect, appears remarkably featureless.

The Milky Way remains conspicuous, though not quite so much in evidence as in January or February.

Chapter Nine

THE STARS OF APRIL

THE SEASONAL CHANGE-OVER in the sky is more or less complete by April evenings. Orion, the symbol of winter, has to all intents and purposes disappeared, though it is true that the northern part of the constellation still lingers above the horizon and does not actually set until about midnight. Aldebaran and Sirius are barely visible, and of the Hunter's retinue only Procyon and the Twins remain prominent—apart from Capella, high in the west. The spring groups such as Boötes, Leo and Virgo have come well into view.

The April charts hold good for:

January 1	4 a.m.	(4 hours G.M.T.)
February 1	2 a.m.	(2 hours G.M.T.)
March 1	midnight	(0 hours G.M.T.)
April 1	10 p.m.	(22 hours G.M.T.; 11 p.m. Summer Time.)
May 1	8 p.m.	(20 hours G.M.T.; 9 p.m. Summer Time.)

The Great Bear is practically overhead, which means that Cepheus and Cassiopeia, on the other side of the Pole Star, are reaching their lowest positions in the north, though they never drop close enough to the horizon to be difficult to find. Vega and Deneb are rising in the north-east, though they have not yet become prominent.

The best way to locate Vega at this time of year is to use Capella and Polaris as pointers. Unfortunately, Vega and Capella are so far apart in the sky that when using hemispherical charts the line joining them appears somewhat "kinked". This is due to the way in which the charts have been drawn, but it does not really matter, since both Vega and Capella are so bright. Now that Sirius is out of the reckoning, no star in the evening sky apart from Arcturus is anything like so brilliant.

The southern aspect is dominated by Leo, the celestial lion. Mythologically, Leo was one of the victims of Hercules, who had been ordered to perform a series of twelve labours which

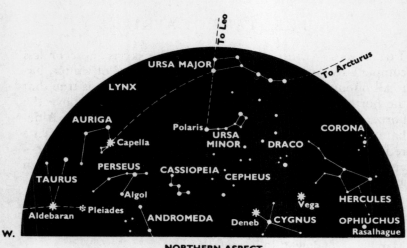

NORTHERN ASPECT

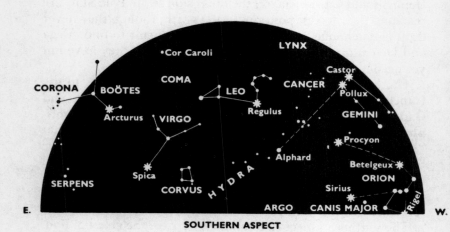

SOUTHERN ASPECT

would have daunted even a demigod. Sent to kill a huge black lion in the marshes of Nemæa, he duly slaughtered the luckless creature and made a cloak out of its skin; in the sky, however, Leo is much more prominent than Hercules himself! Between the Lion and the Twins is a rather obscure group, Cancer (the Crab), whose sole claim to distinction is that it contains a naked-eye cluster. From Cancer the straggly outline of Hydra, the Watersnake, stretches down as far as the horizon, passing underneath Leo, while perched on the snake's back is a crow, Corvus, marked by four moderately bright stars which can be quite conspicuous on a clear April evening.

Arcturus in Boötes and Spica in Virgo are the other first-magnitude stars on view. At this time of the year Arcturus is visible all through the hours of darkness, while Spica does not set until shortly before sunrise.

BOÖTES: *The Herdsman*

Boötes has no really firm legends attached to him, though according to one tale he was a wandering farmer who invented the two-oxen plough and was rewarded with a place in the sky. In any case, the constellation is extremely prominent, and is graced by the presence of Arcturus, the brightest star north of the celestial equator.

The curve of the Great Bear's tail leads straight to Arcturus, but there should never be any difficulty about identification. The magnitude of Arcturus is −0·1, so that it is appreciably brighter than Capella or Vega, and outshines Spica by more than a complete magnitude. Moreover, its colour is pronounced enough to be obvious with the naked eye. It is not really red in the same sense as Betelgeux or Aldebaran, but it is unquestionably light orange. Its surface is cooler than that of the Sun—only a little over 4,000 degrees Centigrade, as against 6,000 degrees—but to make up for this Arcturus is extremely large, with a diameter of roughly 30,000,000 miles. Its distance from us is 36 light-years.

Arcturus is not a "searchlight" in the same sense as Rigel, since it is only 100 times more luminous than the Sun, but it is ranked as a giant star. Viewed through binoculars or a telescope, its colour makes it a glorious sight.

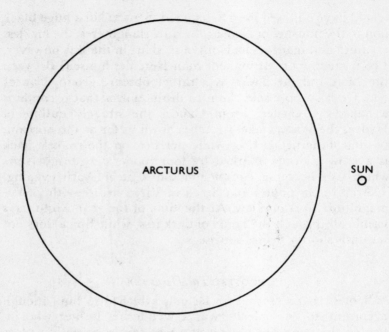

ARCTURUS

SUN
O

Fig. 41. Arcturus compared with the Sun.

The rest of Boötes contains some fairly bright stars, but the pattern seems really to include Alphekka or Alpha Coronæ, leader of the neighbouring constellation of Corona Borealis (the Northern Crown). There is a very noticeable "spoon" outline consisting of Alphekka (2·3) and four of the stars in Boötes; Gamma (3·0), Epsilon (2·4), Arcturus, and Eta (2·7). I have therefore departed from my usual rule of giving a separate chart for each constellation, and have shown Corona together with Boötes.

Most identification charts give a more complex outline for Boötes, putting in several fainter stars to make up the pattern, but it always seems to me that the spoon-shape is easier to recognize. Incidentally, Delta (3·5), in the area between Alphekka and Gamma Boötis, has a faint companion close beside it, visible in binoculars but not with the naked eye.

It is worth taking a closer look at Epsilon, at the top of the spoon-handle. It is of the same colour as Arcturus, but the orange cast is not nearly so evident, since the star is much

fainter; to the unaided eye it looks practically white. It pro
vides a good example of the effect of light-intensity upon
observed colour. Delicate hues which can be quite strong for
bright objects are totally lost when the light-intensity drops;
it is impossible to tell whether a very dim star is red, yellow,
blue or plain white. Epsilon Boötis is reasonably conspicuous,
but even so it is rated two and a quarter magnitudes below
Arcturus. This is why the colour of Arcturus is striking to the

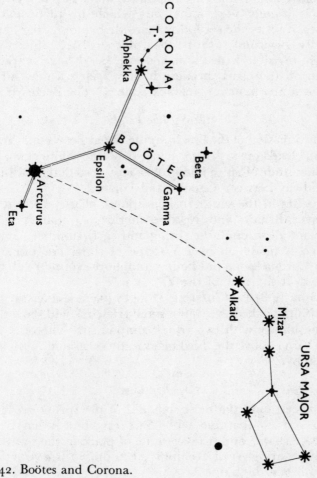

Fig. 42. Boötes and Corona.

hile that of Epsilon is not.

CORONA BOREALIS: *The Northern Crown*

one of the few constellations whose outline bears resemblance to the object named. There is a small semicirclet of stars which could well be interpreted as a crown; Alphekka is almost as bright as Polaris, but the other stars of the semicircle are relatively dim, so that mist or artificial lighting will hide them.

Corona contains one remarkable variable. This is T Coronæ, which is usually very faint, but which in 1866 suddenly brightened up to the second magnitude before fading back to obscurity. A second outburst took place in 1946. Since then it has been invisible with the naked eye, but I have marked its position on the chart, because it may spring a new surprise upon us at any moment. Its nickname is "The Blaze Star".

VIRGO: *The Virgin*

A continuation of the line from the Great Bear's tail through Arcturus leads on to Virgo, marked by the white star Spica. The magnitude of Spica is almost exactly 1, so that in brilliancy it is midway between Capella and Polaris.

Spica lies in the southern hemisphere of the sky, but rises high over Britain and North America, so that it is very prominent all through the spring and early summer. The rest of Virgo is made up of a Y-shape of stars, not unlike the Boötes-Corona spoon but fainter and more symmetrical. Spica is placed at the base of the Y.

Gamma (2·8) is of interest. It looks like a single star when seen with the naked-eye, but a small telescope will show that it is a fine binary with two equal components. The only other star in Virgo above the third magnitude is Epsilon (2·9), at the top of the Y.

LEO: *The Lion*

Leo is certainly the most splendid of the spring groups. It has no star comparable with Arcturus, but it has a very distinctive shape, and it takes pride of place in the south part of the sky during April evenings. At midnight it is practically due south, and high up.

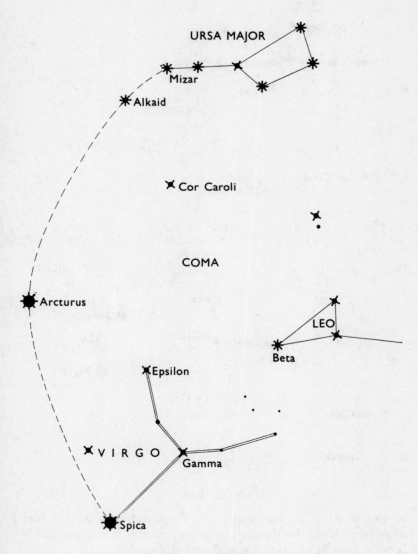

Fig. 43. Virgo.

As a rough guide, it is sufficient to use the Pointers in the Great Bear, since a direction-line away from the Pole Star will arrive in the middle of Leo. To find Regulus, the brightest of the Lion stars, it is more accurate to use Megrez and Phad,

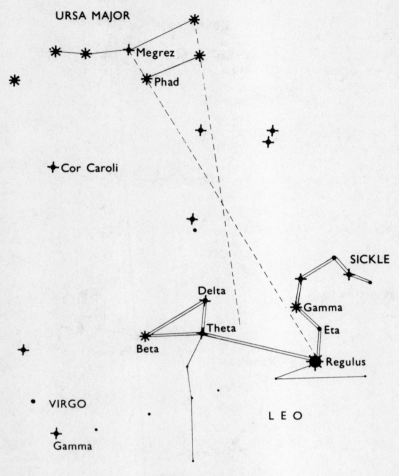

Fig. 44. Leo.

as shown in Fig. 44, but in any case Regulus stands out because of its brightness. Its magnitude is 1·4, so that it is appreciably fainter than Spica, but it is still very noticeable.

Regulus, known in ancient times as the Royal Star, is white. It lies at the lower end of a conspicuous line of stars arranged in a pattern which is not unlike the mirror-image of a question-mark. This curve is the famous Sickle of Leo, and in addition to Regulus it contains Gamma (2·0) together with several more stars of the third and fourth magnitudes.

The Sickle is the most obvious part of Leo, but there is also a well-marked triangle made up of Beta (2·1), Delta (2·6) and Theta (3·3). Beta is an interesting star, because in ancient times it was said to be of the first magnitude, outshining Regulus. Here again we may be dealing with a star which has faded somewhat during the past thousand years or so, and it may be slightly variable over shorter periods, so that I have included it in the list of suspected variables given in the Appendix. Official lists make it about a tenth of a magnitude fainter than Gamma Leonis, in the Sickle, so that to the naked eye the two should appear virtually equal when they are the same distance above the horizon. It takes a skilled observer to detect a magnitude-difference of a tenth of a magnitude, though with practice it can be done.

LEO MINOR: *The Little Lion* and SEXTANS: *The Sextant*

These two constellations, near the Sickle of Leo, were added to the sky by Hevelius in 1690. It hardly seems that they merit separate names, since neither contains any bright stars or obvious outlines, but they have been shown on all star-maps for the past two and a half centuries, so that there is no point in deleting them now.

Both may be found by using the Sickle. Leo Minor lies between Gamma Leonis on the one hand, and the third-magnitude triangle in Ursa Major on the other. To locate Sextans, extend a line from Eta Leonis (3·6) through Regulus, and continue it for twice the distance between the two. Both groups, particularly Sextans, are so dim and barren that few naked-eye observers will take more than a passing interest in them.

COMA BERENICES: *Berenice's Hair*

Yet another faint constellation, but this time a more note-worthy one, is Coma Berenices. It has no star brighter than magnitude 4½, but there are a great many faint ones, and the whole region gives the impression of being a very large, loose star-cluster.

Coma is easy to find when the sky is clear, but the slightest mist will hide it, so that the entire region will appear blank.

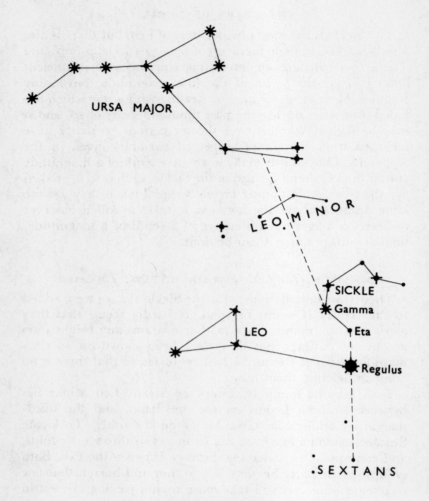

Fig. 45. Leo Minor and Sextans.

The three key stars are Arcturus in Boötes, Cor Caroli in Canes Venatici, and Beta Leonis. These three form a large triangle, within which lies most of Coma. The area of numerous dim stars extends south toward Virgo, entering the "bowl" of the Y. It is well worth sweeping with binoculars.

Coma is not an ancient constellation—it was formed by the Danish astronomer Tycho Brahe, who died in 1601—but the region was studied by the early star-gazers, and a legend is attached to it. According to the story, Queen Berenice of Egypt vowed to cut off her beautiful hair, and place it in the temple of Venus, provided that her husband returned safely from a dangerous war against the Assyrians. When the king came back unharmed, Berenice kept her promise, so impressing the gods that they transferred the shining tresses to the sky.

CANCER: *The Crab*

The area between Castor and Pollux on the one hand and Regulus on the other looks very dull and featureless. It is

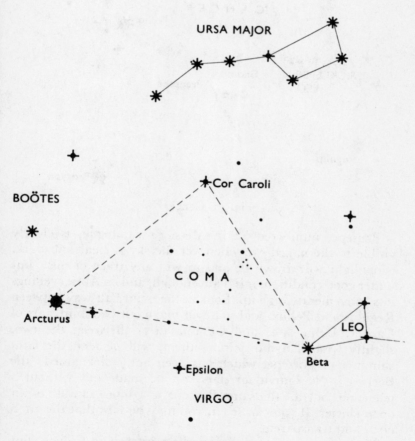

Fig. 46. Coma Berenices.

occupied by Cancer, the celestial crab, which is one of the oldest of the constellations, but which has only one star as bright as the fourth magnitude. Most of it is contained within the triangle formed by Regulus, Pollux and Procyon.

Identification is not difficult, because although Cancer is faint it has at least a definite shape; it looks rather like a very dim and ghostly Orion. Moreover, there is one object of real interest. This is Præsepe, an open star-cluster inferior only to the Pleiades and the Hyades.

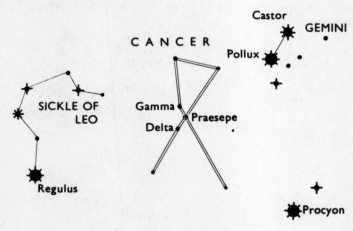

Fig. 47. Cancer.

Præsepe, numbered 44 in Messier's catalogue, is clearly visible to the naked eye whenever the sky is clear and dark. Moonlight will drown it, and so will any trace of mist, but under good conditions it is plain enough, and on April evenings it is conveniently high up. Look at the point half-way between Regulus and Pollux, and you will make out two faint stars of Cancer, Delta (4·2) and Gamma (4·7). Between the two, slightly west of a line joining them, will be seen the faint shimmer of Præsepe, which has been aptly nicknamed "the Beehive". No individual stars can be made out without a telescope, but all the same Præsepe is a fine example of an open cluster. If you can see it, you may be sure that the air is clear and transparent.

There is nothing else of immediate interest in Cancer, but

it is worth noting that the constellation lies in the Zodiac, so that bright planets pass through it from time to time.

HYDRA: *The Watersnake*

It has been said, inelegantly but graphically, that Hydra is "a lot of nothing". Apart from the original Argo it is the largest constellation in the sky, sprawling its way across the southern aspect during April evenings, beginning not far from Procyon and ending below Spica. There is only one bright star, Alphard or Alpha Hydræ (2·0), and there is a remarkable dearth of interesting objects.

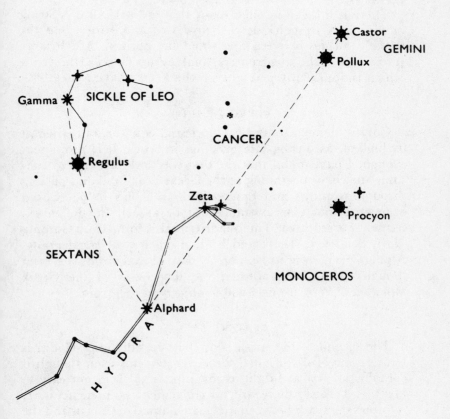

Fig. 48. The Head of Hydra.

Alphard has been called "the Solitary One". There are no conspicuous stars anywhere near it, and for this reason it is easy to find, particularly since it rises to a fair altitude over Britain and North America. It is a Red Giant, 94 light-years away and very much larger and more luminous than the Sun. Its colour is noticeable even with the naked eye, while binoculars bring it out strongly.

Castor and Pollux act as pointers to Alphard; the direction-line crosses part of Cancer on the way, and also passes through the Watersnake's head, which is made up of four stars fairly close together (Zeta Hydræ, the brightest of them, is slightly below the third magnitude). Gamma Leonis and Regulus, in the Sickle, may also be used, as shown in Fig. 48.

There is little to be said about the rest of Hydra. A string of dim stars straggles down below Leo and Virgo, and the snake's tail lies between Spica and the horizon. Much more prominent is the quadrilateral making up Corvus, the Crow which is apparently perching on the Watersnake's back.

CORVUS: *The Crow*

Corvus lies well south of the celestial equator, but when at its highest, as during late evenings in April, it is prominent enough. I have found that the best way to locate it is to continue the curve beginning at the Great Bear's tail and passing through Arcturus and Spica. The curve has to be twisted somewhat, but Corvus stands out because it lies in an extremely barren area. The quadrilateral is formed by Gamma (2·6), Beta (2·7), Delta and Epsilon (each 3·0). Incidentally, Alpha Corvi, close to Epsilon, is only of magnitude 4·2 even though it has been allotted the first letter of the Greek alphabet. There are no notable objects in the group.

CRATER: *The Cup*

The second of the small constellations adjoining Hydra is Crater, one of the original forty-eight groups even though it contains no star as bright as magnitude $3\frac{1}{2}$. It is not easy to identify, because there are no convenient pointers to it. It occupies the space between the quadrilateral of Corvus and the third-magnitude star Nu Hydræ, and consists of a small, dim

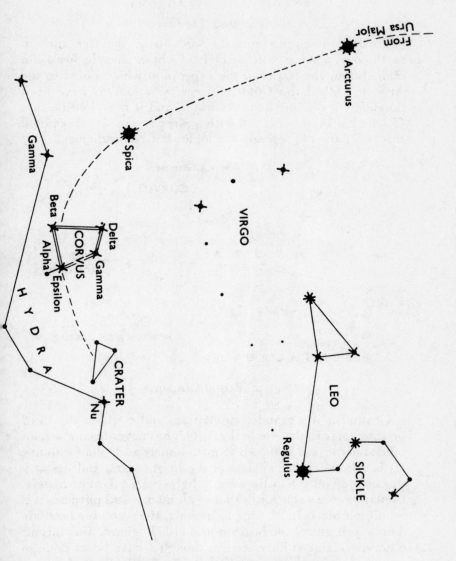

Fig. 49. Corvus, Crater, and the Tail of Hydra.

triangle. The best way to find it is probably to curve up a line from the two lower stars of Corvus, as shown here. Crater, like its neighbours, is entirely unremarkable.

CENTAURUS: *The Centaur*

Finally, something must be said about the Centaur—in mythology, a being with the body of a horse and the head of a man. Jason, the leader of the expedition which sailed in the Argo to collect the Golden Fleece, was said to have been taught by a centaur named Chiron, and it may well be that Chiron has been honoured with a place in the sky, though on this point the old legends are somewhat contradictory.

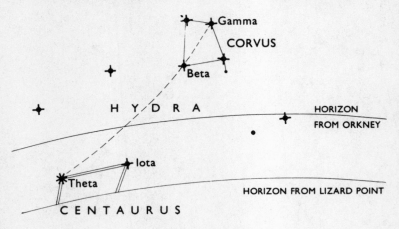

Fig. 50. Part of Centaurus.

Centaurus is a grand constellation, and contains the third brightest star in the whole sky, which has never been given an official name and is known to astronomers as Alpha Centauri. (It is also much the nearest of the bright stars, and lies at a distance of only a little over 4 light-years.) Unfortunately, Centaurus lies so far south that to all intents and purposes it is invisible from Britain. One of its stars, the second-magnitude Theta, just grazes the horizon in South England, and various observers claim to have seen it, though I have never done so myself. I have, however, seen it excellently from Arizona, together with other stars in the northern part of the constellation, and it should be seen from the New York area when at its highest. It is placed almost in a line with two of the stars in Corvus (Gamma and Beta). People who live on the south coast of Devon or Cornwall may care to look for it; midnight in early April is the best possible time, but the chances of success are slight.

Leo, Virgo and their companions in the spring sky compensate in some measure for the loss of Orion, even though they are so much less striking. It is a pity that the brilliant Centaurus is hidden from observers in Europe and North America—but one cannot have everything, and at least there is plenty to see.

Chapter Ten

THE STARS OF MAY

THE MAY CHART is the first in which Orion is absent altogether. The brilliant Hunter has vanished below the horizon, and of his retinue only Capella and the Twins remain. These, fortunately, can be located by using the Great Bear, so that from a direction-finding point of view the loss of Orion is not disastrous.

The times for which the new chart holds good are:

January 1	6 a.m.	(6 hours G.M.T.)
February 1	4 a.m.	(4 hours G.M.T.)
March 1	2 am.	(2 hours G.M.T.)
April 1	midnight	(0 hours G.M.T.) (1 a.m. Summer Time)
May 1	10 p.m.	(22 hours G.M.T.) (11 p.m. Summer Time)

Of course, it is also valid for 20 hours G.M.T. (9 p.m. Summer Time) on June 1, but no stars can then be seen, owing to the lightness of the sky.

On the chart, the Great Bear is more or less overhead, which means that Cassiopeia is at its lowest, well above the northern horizon. Arcturus is high up, and Spica almost due south, with Regulus and the Lion very prominent in the south-west. Castor and Pollux are dropping; the faint outline of Cancer, with the "beehive" cluster Præsepe, can be seen easily enough, together with the whole of Hydra. The Corvus quadrilateral is quite conspicuous in the south when there are no low-lying mists.

Vega has reached a respectable altitude in the north-east, and Deneb in Cygnus is becoming noticeable, though Altair in Aquila, the third of the first-magnitude stars making up the Summer Triangle, has yet to appear. Much of the south-eastern aspect is taken up by the huge, dim groups of Hercules, Ophiuchus (the Serpent-bearer) and Serpens (the Serpent), which are best described under the July heading because they are then at their highest. Another dim constellation is Libra,

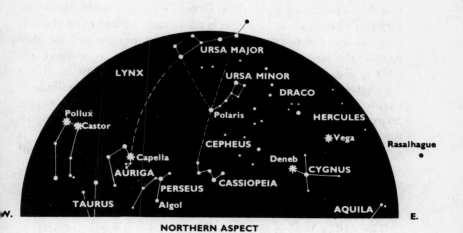

NORTHERN ASPECT

SOUTHERN ASPECT

the Balance, which is notable only because it lies in the Zodiac.

Going back for a moment to our circumpolar groups, it is worth mentioning here that Draco is well placed, and the Dragon's head, close to Vega, is quite easy to find even though its stars are not particularly bright. Most people will be able to split the wide double Nu Draconis, referred to on page 48.

It is also of interest to compare Vega with Capella. Since these two splendid stars are of equal brilliancy, the effects of extinction will tip the scales in favour of whichever one happens to be higher. During May evenings Arcturus will appear brighter than either, partly because its altitude is greater and partly because it really is superior by about two-tenths of a magnitude. The colours of these three northern stars are obviously different; it is impossible to confuse the orange cast of Arcturus with the yellowness of Capella or the steely blue of Vega.

The Milky Way is not so well placed as on earlier charts. It is lower in the sky, and of course the period of darkness is shorter. However, it is still quite spectacular whenever the Moon is absent. Lastly, do not forget Scorpio, the Scorpion, which is just starting to rise. Its leading star, the fiery red Antares, comes into view around midnight, and is very conspicuous during the early hours of the morning. It cannot be shown on the charts given for May, but it appears on those which follow.

Chapter Eleven

THE STARS OF JUNE

JUNE CAN BE a somewhat depressing month for the would-be star gazer who is disinclined to keep late hours. Official twilight lasts all night over Britain; from London the Sun does not set until well after 9 p.m. Summer Time, though from New York things are not so extreme. There is no proper darkness at all whenever the Moon is near full, and the combination of moonlight with constant twilight is crippling.

Yet those people who live further north are even worse off if they are anxious to keep watch on the stars. Not long ago I remember spending a June fortnight in Iceland, when the sky was always too light for any stars to be seen. Neither will I forget a conversation I had with some Russian astronomers when I was in Leningrad, at the famous Pulkovo Observatory. They complained that during the May to August period the sky was hopelessly bright for stellar work, while as soon as the nights lengthened the clouds and mists took charge. I was not surprised to learn that the Russians propose to erect their new telescopes in more southerly parts of the Soviet Union!

It is sometimes hard to remember that during June, when the northern hemisphere is enjoying its summer, the Earth is at its greatest distance from the Sun—$94\frac{1}{2}$ million miles, as against $91\frac{1}{2}$ million miles just before Christmas. The seasons have very little to do with sheer distance. During northern summer, the Earth's northern hemisphere is tilted toward the Sun, and so receives the full benefit of solar radiation.

Timings for the June chart are as follows:

February 1	6 a.m.	(6 hours G.M.T.)	
March 1	4 a.m.	(4 hours G.M.T.)	
April 1	2 a.m.	(2 hours G.M.T.)	(3 a.m. Summer Time)
May 1	midnight	(0 hours G.M.T.)	(1 a.m. Summer Time)
June 1	10 p.m.	(22 hours G.M.T.)	(11 p.m. Summer Time)
July 1	8 p.m.	(20 hours G.M.T.)	(9 p.m. Summer Time)

The Great Bear has shifted to a point somewhat westward

NORTHERN ASPECT

SOUTHERN ASPECT

of the zenith, but is still very high up; Cassiopeia has gained altitude in the east, while all three first-magnitude stars of the "Summer Triangle" (Vega, Deneb and Altair) are also easterly. Arcturus is almost due south, very high up, while Leo and Virgo are dropping westward; Corvus may still be quite prominent when the sky is clear and moonless. In the west, Castor and Pollux are now too low to be conspicuous, and Capella is not much in evidence. The large, faint groups Hercules, Ophiuchus and Serpens occupy much of the south-east.

However, there has been a brilliant newcomer; Antares in Scorpio, known as "the Rival of Mars" because of its fiery hue. Deneb and Vega act as rough pointers to it, but this is not well shown in the hemispherical charts, because Deneb and Vega have to be drawn on the northern aspect and Antares on the southern. It is a pity that the Scorpion never shows up well in British latitudes; it is a grand constellation when properly seen. Observers in the more southerly parts of the United States have much better views of it.

The Milky Way is not seen to advantage in June, partly because it is relatively low down but mainly because the sky is not dark enough.

Chapter Twelve

THE STARS OF JULY

THE CHART FOR July is a logical development of that for
June. The spring groups such as Leo and Virgo are setting,
while the autumn constellation Pegasus has made its appearance in the east. It is rather unfortunate that large, faint
groups occupy so much of the southern aspect, but at least
Antares is there, shining redly from the low south, while the
richest part of the Milky Way is also on view. The charts
apply to:

March 1	6 a.m.	(6 hours G.M.T.)	
April 1	4 a.m.	(4 hours G.M.T.)	(5 a.m. Summer Time)
May 1	2 a.m.	(2 hours G.M.T.)	(3 a.m. Summer Time)
June 1	midnight	(0 hours G.M.T.)	(1 a.m. Summer Time)
July 1	10 p.m.	(22 hours G.M.T.)	(11 p.m. Summer Time)
August 1	8 p.m.	(20 hours G.M.T.)	(9 p.m. Summer Time)

In the northern aspect the Great Bear is still very high up,
but now lies west of the zenith, which means that Cassiopeia
has gained altitude in the north-east. Arcturus is still very
much in evidence, though Spica has well passed its best.

A glance at the two hemispherical maps brings home another
of their limitations. As has been noted, the Great Bear's tail
points toward Arcturus (Fig. 42), and this is obvious when
the groups are seen in the sky. The hemispherical maps confuse
it badly, because the Bear and Arcturus have to be shown on
different charts. Unfortunately there is no solution without
reverting to the usual circular maps, which are probably more
accurate but which are not of much use in helping the
beginner to identify the constellations.

Vega continues to shine down almost from the overhead
point, while Capella, in the north, is so low that it is difficult
to find; it should be visible from Britain, but not from the New
York area, from which it will have dipped below the horizon.
Regulus has to all intents and purposes vanished in the west,
while the Square of Pegasus, Andromeda and Perseus are just

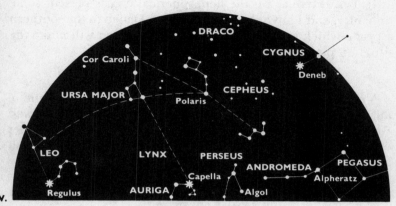

NORTHERN ASPECT

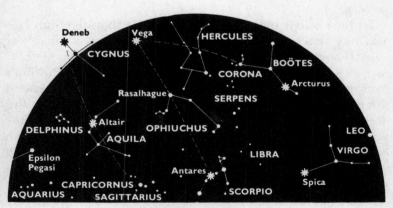

SOUTHERN ASPECT

about observable in the east. I do not propose to say more about Pegasus here, since it so definitely belongs to the autumn, but by midnight in July it has become quite prominent.

The "Summer Triangle" of Vega, Deneb and Altair is now at its best. Here again the hemispherical charts present some difficulty, and I have cheated by adding Deneb to the southern aspect—which is not strictly correct, but which will make the situation plainer.

LYRA: *The Lyre*

Vega is quite unmistakable. It is the equal of Capella, and of all the stars visible from northern countries only Sirius and Arcturus surpass it. It occupies the zenith during summer evenings, and its brilliance, together with its obviously bluish hue, makes it stand out at once.

This is fortunate, because there are no convenient pointers to it. It may be found from the Great Bear, by the rather awkward method of starting at Phad and directing a guide-line between Megrez and Alioth; it also lies in a line with Capella and Polaris, though this is not of much help when Capella is virtually out of view. At any rate, I doubt whether anyone will have much trouble. If, on a summer evening, you look straight upward and see a very bright star, it can only be Vega.

Its blue colour indicates that it is hotter than the Sun. It is also fifty times as luminous, so that it ranks as a giant star even though it is very feeble compared with "searchlights" such as Rigel in Orion. Its distance is $26\frac{1}{2}$ light-years. The Sun's own motion in the Galaxy is carrying it in the general direction of Vega at a rate of 13 miles per second, but this does not mean that there is any danger of a collision on the line; to cover $26\frac{1}{2}$ light-years (roughly 150 million million miles) would take an extremely long time even at this high velocity, and in any case Vega will not wait for us. Its own motion will have carried it far away long before the Sun arrives in that part of the Galaxy where Vega now lies.

Vega is one of the loveliest of the bright stars; binoculars bring out its blueness very well. The rest of the little constellation of the Lyre is not conspicuous, but it contains more than an average share of interesting objects.

I. The Celestial Pole

The exposure given was 30 minutes, at f/6; Polaris, close to the centre, is clearly not precisely at the pole. The diagonal trail is that of a meteor which crossed the area while the exposure was being made.

II. *The Great Bear, photographed with different exposures*

(A): 5 minute exposure at f/3·5, with an unguided camera.
(B): 20 minute exposure, with a driven camera; the many faint stars come out clearly.

III. Star Trails

Photographs by
Robert Aylott,
with an unguided
camera.
(*Right*) The Great
Bear; exposure
10 minutes at f/3·5.
The trails are
clearly longer than
in Plate II*a*.
(*Lower*) Cassiopeia;
exposure 45
minutes at f/11.
The trails are
longer still.

IV. *The Nature of a Constellation*

This demonstration, carried out in a BBC television studio in 1965, shows the "lining up" of stars to produce a constellation pattern. In a large board, we fixed globes on supports to represent the constellation Leo, putting the stars at the right relative distances from the observer. *Upper:* View from Earth—the outline of Leo is unmistakable.   *Left :* from another angle, as can be seen from the positions of Lawrence Clarke (left) and Matthew Clarke (right), who had not moved; the outline of Leo is lost. *Right :* yet another angle. This shows that the Leo pattern will be seen only from our own particular position in space.

V.

(A): Star-fields in the Milky Way, photographed at Mount Wilson with a 5 in. lens.

(B): Trails of the Moon and Venus, photographed on October 29 1964, with an unguided camera; 30 min. exposure, f/22, FP3, yellow filter.

VI. Jupiter, The Pleiades, The Hyades and Aldebaran

Photographed with a driven camera in 1965. Aldebaran and the V-shape of the Hyades are shown to the lower left; the Pleiades are almost central, with Jupiter to the lower right.

VII. (A) *The Total Solar Eclipse of February 15 1961*

Photographed at Mount Jastrebac in Jugoslavia. (*Left*) the "Diamond Ring" effect. (*Right*) Mid-totality.

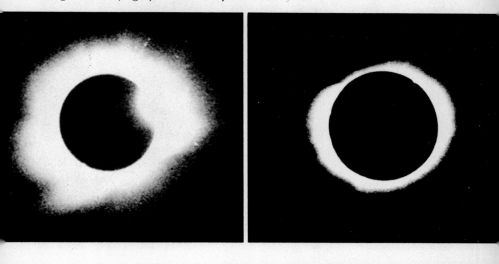

(B) *The Midnight Sun*

Photographed by Patrick Moore from off the coast at North Cape, Norway, in 1961. The Sun can be seen on the horizon. This photograph was taken at midnight.

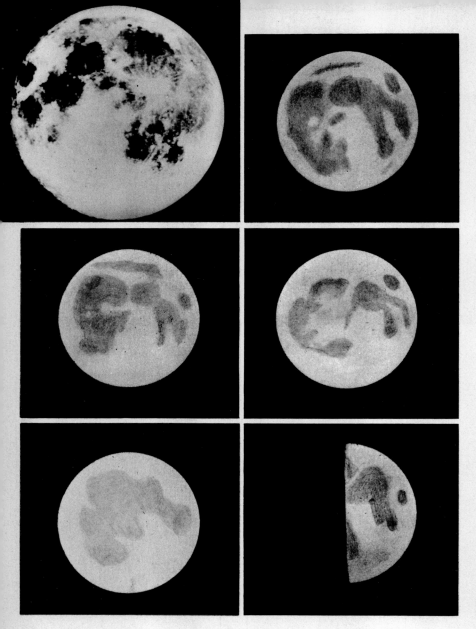

VIII. The Moon

Upper Left: a photograph taken with a small telescope. The remainder are drawings made with the naked eye: Patrick Moore (*upper right*), Iain Nicolson (*mid-left*), Pamela Pyer (*mid-right*), Terry Lock (*lower left*), Christopher Hardy (*lower right*). Considerable detail is shown, and the agreement is very fair. These are typical of many naked-eye drawings of the Moon made at the author's request in 1965.

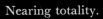

IX. The Lunar Eclipse of December 19 1964

Nearing totality.

The approach of the Earth's shadow.

X. Comet Cunningham

Photographed on December 21 1940, from Mount Wilson with a 5 in. Ross lens. The camera was guided to follow the comet, so that the stars are drawn out into trails. The comet was visible to the naked eye as a dim, misty blur.

Aerial view.

XI. Meteor Crater, Arizona

The author standing on the crest of the crater wall.

XII. Trail of Echo II

Photographed on April 30 1965, 21.55, at Selsey. The Great Bear may be seen at the bottom of the plate. Unguided camera.

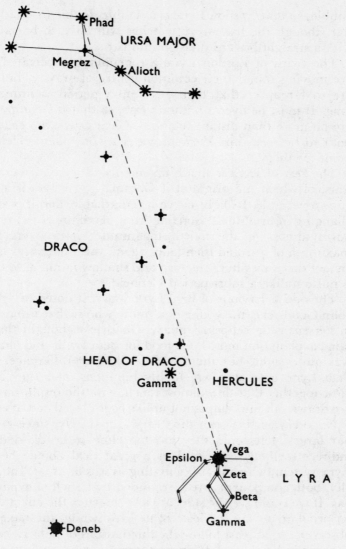

Fig. 51. Lyra.

First there is the famous naked-eye double Epsilon Lyræ, which may be found close to Vega. Normal-sighted people will be able to see that it is made up of two 4½-magnitude stars side by side. Telescopically, each component is again

115

double, so that Epsilon Lyræ is a double-double or quadruple star, though the naked-eye watcher will have to be satisfied with a straightforward division into two.

The twins of Epsilon Lyræ are genuinely associated, and are moving round their common centre of gravity, but they are so far apart that their revolution period is immensely long. It must be over a million years, so that the components are no more than distant relations. Clear skies are needed for both to be seen, but Vega provides a convenient reference-point for them.

The rest of Lyra is made up mainly of a quadrilateral of stars, of which the brightest is Gamma (3·2). Beta is a well-known variable. Its light-curve is remarkable, and it is always changing in brightness. Starting from maximum (3·4) it fades down almost to the fourth magnitude; it recovers to its maximum of 3·4, and then fades again, this time as far as 4·4. In fact there are alternate deep and shallow minima, so that it is quite unlike a short-period Cepheid.

The odd behaviour of Beta Lyræ was first noted in 1784 by John Goodricke, the young deaf-mute who realized that Algol in Perseus is an eclipsing binary. Goodricke thought that the same explanation must hold good for Beta Lyræ, and again he was quite right, but there is an important difference. With Beta Lyræ both stars are highly luminous, and they are so close together that they almost touch, with the result that both are drawn out into shapes not unlike eggs placed end to end.

Nobody has ever seen the "eggs" separately, since even in our largest telescopes they are too close to be divided, but indirect methods have told us a great deal about the Beta Lyræ system, which is as fascinating as it is unusual. Incidentally, both components are surrounded by a shell of expanding gas. If we could see the stars at close quarters the effect would be peculiar, to say the least of it. Meanwhile, the naked-eye observer can at least follow the fluctuations of Beta Lyræ as it changes in brightness, taking a total of almost 13 days to run through its full cycle. Gamma makes an excellent comparison star, together with another near neighbour, Zeta (4·1).

There are other noteworthy features in Lyra. In particular there is a fine example of what is known, misleadingly, as a planetary nebula—in actual fact a faint, hot star with an

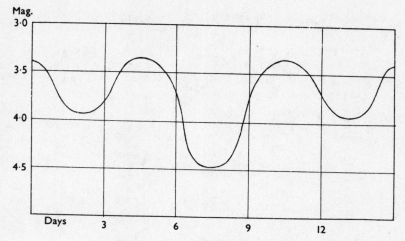

Fig. 52. Light-curve of Beta Lyræ.

immense gasous "atmosphere". The brightest planetary nebula in the sky lies directly between Beta and Gamma Lyræ,
but since it is not visible without a telescope it need concern us
no more for the present.

CYGNUS: *The Swan*

The celestial swan is more often, and more appropriately,
termed the Northern Cross, since its X-shaped pattern is
striking. Deneb, its leading star, is of the first magnitude, but
since it is ranked as 1·3 it is more than a full magnitude
fainter than Vega.

Appearances are deceptive. Deneb is one of our "searchlights", and is so remote that the light from it now reaching
Earth started on its journey at the time when the Romans still
occupied Britain. Its exact candle-power is uncertain, but it
must be as powerful as at least 10,000 Suns put together. It is
slightly yellowish, though to the naked eye it appears colourless.

Together with Vega in Lyra and Altair in Aquila, Deneb
makes up the "Summer Triangle". Again there are no convenient pointers to it, but if necessary two of the stars in the W
of Cassiopeia may be pressed into service, as may be seen

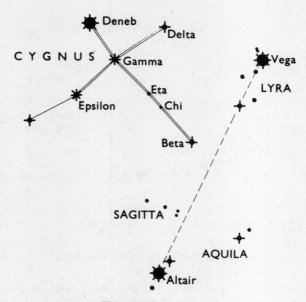

Fig. 53. Cygnus.

from the maps. On the July chart it lies rather east of Vega, and almost as high up.

The cross of Cygnus is marked by Deneb together with four other stars, Gamma (2·2), Epsilon (2·5), Delta (2·9) and Beta (3·1). Of these, Beta, often known by its proper name of Albireo, is the most interesting. It is fainter than the rest, and further from the middle of the X, so that it spoils the symmetry of the pattern, but to compensate for this it is a glorious telescopic double, with a yellow primary and a bluish or greenish companion. A good way to identify it is to remember that it lies not far off the line joining Vega to Altair.

Half-way between Beta and Gamma lies a fourth-magnitude star, Eta Cygni. At times a similar star may be seen close to it. This is Chi Cygni, a variable quite different in nature from the Cepheids or the Algol-type eclipsing binaries. It has a long period, amounting to more than 400 days, and it has a considerable range in brightness. At its best it may equal Eta, but at near minimum it becomes so dim that large telescopes are needed to show it at all. It is visible to the naked eye for only a few weeks during its cycle, so that normally the observer who lacks a telescope will not see it, but it is always worth looking for. Yearly almanacs give the times when it should be visible.

Chi Cygni is a typical long-period variable. Like most of its kind, it is strongly red, though its light-intensity is too low for the colour to be seen with the naked eye. I shall have more to say about variables of this sort when discussing the "Wonderful Star" Mira, which lies in the constellation of Cetus and is definitely an autumn object.

The Milky Way passes straight through Cygnus, running from Cassiopeia in the north-east and continuing into Aquila. The milkiness is particularly strong in Cygnus, and it is easy to see that the shining band divides into two portions, one branch petering out after some distance while the other extends over the horizon. There are many glorious star-fields, and altogether Cygnus is one of the most spectacular regions in the whole northern sky.

AQUILA: *The Eagle*

Altair, leader of the Eagle, is the last member of the "Summer Triangle". Unlike Deneb and Vega, it is not circumpolar anywhere in Britain or the U.S.A.; it passes well below the horizon, though on our July chart it is high up, somewhat east of south. Alkaid, in the Great Bear, may be used as a guide-star together with Vega, but the distance is considerable—half-way across the sky—and once Vega and Deneb have been found, Altair should follow at once, particularly as it has a fainter star to either side of it.

Altair is one of our nearest neighbours in space. It is a mere 16 light-years off, and nine times as luminous as the Sun, so that it is a very minor star compared with Deneb. Yet it has a hot surface, and is pure white.

Aquila itself really does give a slight impression of a bird in flight. Several of its stars are of above magnitude $3\frac{1}{2}$, though none can rival Altair, and the general pattern is quite distinctive. Flanking Altair are Gamma (2·7) and Beta (3·9); Gamma is reddish, and I have found that the colour may just be noticed with the naked eye.

Below the Altair chain lie three more stars, Theta (3·3), Eta (variable) and Delta (3·4), arranged in a line. Eta Aquilæ

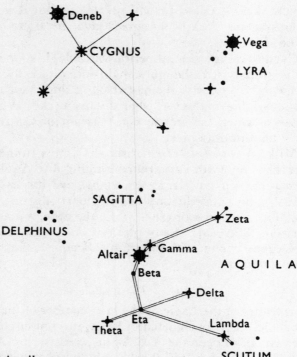

Fig. 54. Aquila.

is a Cepheid, fluctuating between magnitudes 3·7 and 4·5 in a period of just over 7 days; Beta makes a good comparison star. Because Eta Aquilæ has a period which is longer than that of the prototype variable Delta Cephei (5·4 days), it follows that it is more luminous. With Cepheids, the longer the period, the more powerful the star.

Aquila, like Cygnus, is involved in the Milky Way; the main branch goes straight through it, passing by Altair and continuing to the last fairly bright star in the constellation, Lambda (3·4). This provides an extra means of locating Aquila, provided that the sky is sufficiently dark and clear for the Milky Way to be seen.

SCUTUM SOBIESKII: *Sobieski's Shield*

Hevelius, the seventeenth-century astronomer who produced a good star catalogue, had a passion for inventing new constellations. In this he was not alone, but many of his additions have survived, whereas most of those proposed by his contemporaries have been tacitly dropped.

Hevelius wanted to do honour to John Sobieski, King of Poland, who had defeated the Turkish Army at the walls of Vienna. Accordingly, he separated off a small part of Aquila, close to Lambda, and named it after Sobieski's coat of arms. The result is utterly formless, and there are no stars in the constellation as bright as the fourth magnitude, so that it does not merit a separate name.

However, Scutum has become firmly established as an independent group, and it does at least contain a bright section of the Milky Way. There is also one open cluster, No. 11 in Messier's list, which is visible with the naked eye; telescopically it is a lovely sight, and is often nicknamed "the Wild Duck". Look for it a short distance from Lambda Aquilæ, and you will probably see it, but it appears only as a small patch, and the Milky Way is so bright nearby that identification of the cluster can be troublesome. There is no point in giving a special chart for Scutum, so I have included it together with the map of Aquila.

DELPHINUS: *The Dolphin*

The area enclosed by imaginary lines joining Deneb, Vega, Altair and Epsilon Pegasi contains four small constellations, of which three are "original" and the last "modern". Epsilon Pegasi does not belong to the Square of Pegasus, but is included in the main constellation, and so must be deferred until our autumn chart. It is slightly less bright than Polaris; during late evenings in July it is well above the eastern horizon.

Of the small constellations, the only one which may be recognized at once is Delphinus. Its brightest stars are only slightly above the fourth magnitude, but there is a compact little group of them, appearing almost like a very loose cluster; in shape, the Dolphin bears a vague resemblance to a tiny, dim and distorted Plough. An attractive legend is associated with it. It is said that Arion, a celebrated musician of ancient times, was sailing home together with some rich prizes he had won for his singing and playing, when he was attacked by the ship's crew and thrown into the sea. Luckily for him, a friendly

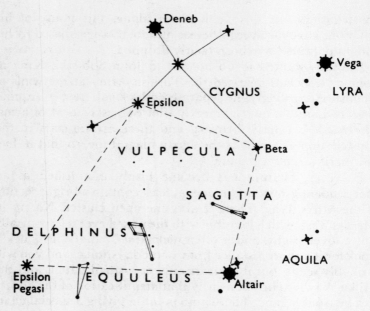

Fig. 55. Equuleus, Delphinus, Sagitta and Vulpecula.

dolphin had been so charmed by Arion's songs that he collected the hapless musician and took him to port, after which he was very properly placed in the sky "for services rendered".

Delphinus is easy to find, because of its compactness, but on the whole this is an infuriating area; nothing seems to point to anything. Moreover, any semblance of mist will hide the faint stars, so that the entire region will appear blank. A line from Deneb passed through Epsilon Cygni, in the X, and continued for some way on the far side will arrive near Delphinus, but the alignment is not particularly good.

EQUULEUS: *The Little Horse*

Equuleus, despite its status as one of Ptolemy's constellations, is extremely obscure. Its stars are even fainter than those of Delphinus, and there is no crowding together. Look slightly below a line joining Delphinus to Epsilon Pegasi, and you will be able to make out the faint triangle marking Equuleus, but there is nothing here of interest to the naked-eye observer.

SAGITTA: *The Arrow*

This is another ancient constellation. Only two of its stars attain the fourth magnitude, but there is at least a distinctive shape, and it is not too difficult to conjure up the picture of an arrow. There is no serious danger of confusing Sagitta with Delphinus, because Sagitta lies almost midway between Altair and Beta Cygni; in any case, it does not give the same impression of a very open cluster. The Milky Way runs straight through Sagitta, so that the whole area is rather rich.

VULPECULA: *The Fox*

For one we have a small, obscure constellation which is not ancient. Vulpecula—formerly Vulpecula et Anser, the Fox and Goose—was created by Hevelius, though for no good reason. It lies between Sagitta and Delphinus to the one side, and Cygnus to the other, but will not easily be identified, as it has no stars as bright as the fourth magnitude. There is one remarkable object, the so-called Dumb-bell Nebula, well below naked-eye visibility.

It is worth mentioning, as an aside, that in 1670 a third-magnitude nova flared up in Vulpecula, not far from Beta Cygni. This is not surprising; most novæ appear in or near the Milky Way, and Vulpecula is contained in the main stream running from Cygnus is the direction of Aquila.

HERCULES

During late evenings in summer much of the southern aspect of the sky, extending almost to the zenith, is taken up with three large, formless constellations—Hercules, the great hero of mythology; Ophiuchus, the Serpent-bearer; and Serpens, the snake with which Ophiuchus is struggling. I always feel that this is one of the most confusing regions in the sky. There are no well-marked patterns; there is only one brightish star, Alpha Ophiuchi; and the three constellations are hopelessly intertwined, so that it may take the beginner some time to sort them out.

Hercules should have pride of place, as being the most northerly, but the key-star to the area is undoubtedly Alpha Ophiuchi (2·1), sometimes still called by its old proper name

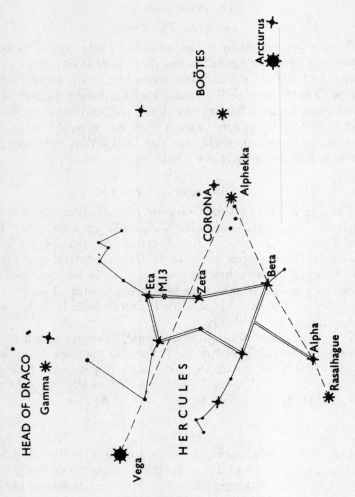

Fig. 56. Hercules.

of Rasalhague. It makes up a large quadrilateral together with Vega, Deneb and Altair, and on our July charts it is almost due south, fairly high up. There is nothing striking about it, and I have never found any satisfactory pointers to help in recognizing it, but at least it is fairly prominent, because it lies in a barren region.

As for Hercules, it lies mainly between Vega and Arcturus—

or, more precisely, between Vega and the leader of the Northern Crown, Alpha Coronæ. It is large, and sprawls southward for some distance, but its two brightest stars, Beta and Zeta, are only of magnitude 2·8. The shape of the constellation is so nebulous that it may be interpreted in several different ways. However, it contains two notable objects which should certainly be described.

The first is a star-cluster of a type quite different from the Pleiades, Hyades or Præsepe. It is known as M.13 (the thirteenth in Messier's list), and is termed a "globular", since its hundred thousand stars are arranged in the form of a vast sphere. It is the only globular cluster visible to the naked eye from Europe or the United States; there are two globulars which are brighter, but both lie in the far south.

M.13 is a very elusive object to the naked eye, and may be seen only when the sky is both perfectly clear and absolutely dark. The guide-star is Zeta Herculis (2·8). North of Zeta lies the fainter star Eta (3·5); the globular lies directly between the two, rather closer to Eta.

The main trouble is in identifying the key-stars. Probably the best way is to locate Vega and Alpha Coronæ, and join them with an imaginary line. Look mid-way along this line; slightly below it you will see Zeta Herculis, after which Eta should present no difficulties. If conditions are good enough, the cluster will appear as a very faint, tiny patch. Telescopes will resolve it into stars (it is a superb sight with the reflector in my own observatory), but the naked-eye observer who has no prior knowledge could not possibly guess its true nature.

About a hundred globulars are known, each containing around a hundred thousand stars. They are extremely remote —the Hercules cluster, for instance, lies at 34,000 light-years— and make up a kind of outer framework to the Galaxy, as shown in Fig. 57. For many years nobody was able to measure their distances, but then, about 1920, the American astronomer Harlow Shapley found Cepheid variables in them. By watching the Cepheids, Shapley was able to work out their distances, and before long he drew up the first accurate plan of the shape of the Galaxy. Also, he realized that since most of the globulars lie in the southern part of the sky, our own position must be well away from the centre of the Galaxy. He was right in every

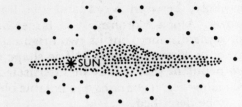

Fig. 57. The Globular Clusters—which make
up a sort of outer framework to the Galaxy.

detail, and his investigation was one of the most brilliant in the
story of modern astronomy.

The Hercules cluster seems insignificant enough when seen
with the naked eye, and any trace of mist will hide it, but it
has proved to be a vast system of suns much more closely
packed than is usual in the Galaxy—though, of course, they
are still thousands of millions of miles apart. If our Sun were
situated near the middle of a globular cluster, the night-sky
would be magnificent. There would be hundreds of stars
shining more brightly than Sirius does to us, and there would
be no proper darkness even when the Sun dropped below the
horizon.

The second notable object is Alpha Herculis, or Rasalgethi.
It will be found close to Rasalhague in Ophiuchus; the names
are confusingly alike, but the stars are not. Alpha Herculis is a
magnitude the fainter, and is red, though its colour is barely
detectable with the naked eye.

Alpha Herculis is an irregular variable. It changes slowly
and unpredictably between magnitudes $3\frac{1}{4}$ and $3\frac{3}{4}$, and its
fluctuations may be followed without optical aid, particularly
as there are several useful comparison stars not far off. It is
the same kind of variable as Betelgeux in Orion, though it is
not so luminous and is "only" 410 light-years away. Like
Betelgeux, it is of tremendous size.

I always feel that Alpha Herculis, rather separated from the
rest of the constellation, should really have been included in
Ophiuchus. In any case, its brighter neighbour Alpha Ophiuchi is the best guide to it. It is worth adding that Alpha
Ophiuchi, Alpha Herculis, Beta Herculis, and Alpha Coronæ
in the Northern Crown lie in a roughly straight line.

Some time ago I pointed out Alpha Herculis to a dozen

teenage beginners. I asked them to look at it carefully and tell me if they could notice anything unusual about it. None of them realized that it was coloured; and even when I told them, only one boy could see the red tint. With the telescope, of course, it was a very different story, and they all agreed that the colour could not possibly be overlooked. As I have stressed earlier, colour in a star can be seen only when the star is bright enough. All faint stars look white!

In 1934 a British amateur astronomer, J. P. M. Prentice, discovered a bright nova in Hercules, in that part of the constellation near Vega and the Dragon's head. For a few weeks it quite altered the look of that part of the sky, but nowadays it is a very faint telescopic object; its brief glory belongs to the past.

OPHIUCHUS: *The Serpent Bearer*

Ophiuchus contains several brightish stars. As well as Alpha (2·1) there are eight more above magnitude 3·5, but there is no well-marked pattern, and most of the constellation is decidedly barren.

Alpha makes up a sort of kite-shape with Vega, Altair and Deneb, but probably the best way to check on it is to look directly between Altair and Arcturus, rather closer to Altair. Alpha Ophiuchi is the brightest star anywhere in this region, and so should be identifiable, even though the considerable distance between Altair and Arcturus makes the method rather inconvenient.

Alpha Ophiuchi is one of a triangle of stars, the other two being Kappa (3·2) and the red variable Alpha Herculis. There are two other parts of Ophiuchus recognizable without difficulty. The little group of five stars below Alpha, of which Beta (2·8) is the brightest, is quite conspicuous; further south lies a curved line of four stars, of which Delta (2·7) and Epsilon (3·2) make up a noticeable pair. Ophiuchus covers a large area, but it contains nothing of real interest to the naked-eye watcher.

SERPENS: *The Serpent*

Serpens is a peculiar constellation, since it consists of two separate parts. It is meant to represent the snake with which

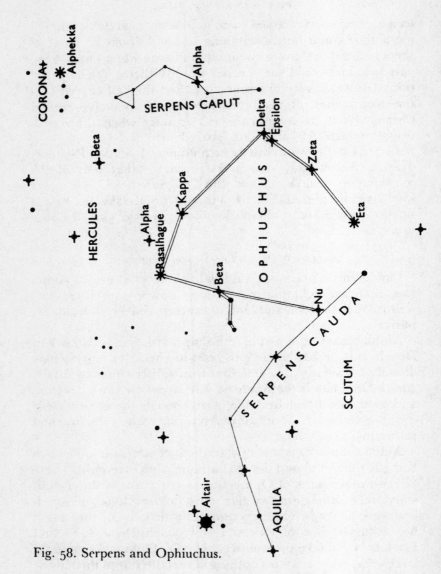

Fig. 58. Serpens and Ophiuchus.

Ophiuchus has been doing battle, and it seems to have had the worst of the argument, since it has been pulled in half. The head (Serpens Caput) lies to one side of Ophiuchus, and the body (Serpens Cauda) to the other.

The head section is the more conspicuous. It begins with a

small triangle of stars below Alpha Coronæ, and fi
line extends southward, including Alpha (2·6); Alpl
less continues the lower curve of Ophiuchus. Serpe
which lies between Ophiuchus and Aquila, is en
remarkable, as it contains only one star above magr
For obvious reasons, I have charted Serpens toget... with
Ophiuchus.

Unravelling this dim, chaotic area takes a good deal of
patience, but at least it is reasonably high up. On the July
chart, it is practically due south.

SCORPIO: *The Scorpion*

Look low in the south during a late evening in July, and
you can hardly fail to notice a star which is not only very
bright, but also very red. This is Antares, in Scorpio. Its name
means "the Rival of Mars"—the Greek name for Mars was
"Ares"—and it is certainly the ruddiest of the first-magnitude
stars.

Antares lies well away from any of our useful pointers, but
this does not much matter, as there is no star of comparable
brilliancy anywhere near it. Deneb and Vega give an approximate line to it, though this is distorted on the hemispherical
charts. Like Altair, Antares is flanked by two fainter stars,
though here the line-of-three is not so straight.

Antares has many claims to fame. It is a large and luminous
Red Giant, more than 3,000 times as powerful as the Sun and
with a diameter of some 300 million miles, so that it is even
vaster than Betelgeux. It is 350 light-years away, so that we
are now seeing it as it used to be in the days when William
Shakespeare was alive. Also it has a faint green companion,
though this is the concern of telescopic observers only.

The only point of regret to Britons and North Americans
(or, to be more specific, "north North Americans") is that
Antares never rises high above the horizon, so that low-lying
haze will obscure it. This also applies to the rest of Scorpio,
which is a magnificent constellation when properly visible.
Since it has a distinctive outline, and is made up of chains of
stars, it is extremely easy to recognize as soon as Antares itself
has been found.

The Scorpion's head consists of several bright stars, arranged

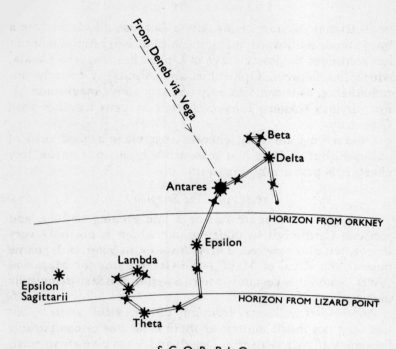

SCORPIO

Fig. 59. Scorpio.

in a roughly north-south line, of which Delta (2·3) and Beta
(2·6) are the most conspicuous. A second line, decidedly
curved, runs down toward the horizon, and includes Antares.

The British horizon cuts off Scorpio half-way, and the
brilliant "sting", of which one member, Lambda (1·6) is the
equal of Castor in Gemini, never rises at all. In the chart, I
have put in the limiting horizon lines for the latitudes of
Orkney and Lizard Point—the extremes of Great Britain.
From the southern United States all of Scorpio can be seen,
even to Theta (1·9). I remember my first view of the complete
group; it was from Arizona, on a pitch-dark night, and I was
suitably impressed. Moreover, Scorpio is involved in the
Milky Way, so that it is exceptionally rich.

SAGITTARIUS: *The Archer*

Next to Scorpio lies Sagittarius, the celestial archer. Like

Scorpio, it belongs to the Zodiac and is crossed by the Milky Way; also like Scorpio, it is too far south to be well seen from Europe or the northern United States, and I have put in the horizon limits as before.

Sagittarius has a number of rather bright stars, but is not too easy to recognize, because of its lack of any well-defined pattern. If Antares can be seen, simply look to the east along the horizon. During July evenings this is straightforward enough, but if Antares is not available (as in late August, for example) the only solution is to use Deneb and Altair as guides. Continue the direction-line down toward the horizon, and you will come to Sagittarius.

The northern part of the group contains one bright star, Sigma (2·1) and several others of above the third magnitude. Further south, to all intents and purposes invisible from Britain but rising in New York, is Epsilon (1·8), leader of the constellation. But the main glory of Sagittarius lies in the star-clouds which make up this part of the Milky Way.

When we turn our eyes toward the Sagittarius star-clouds, we are in fact looking toward the very centre of the Galaxy. The actual centre cannot be seen, because there is too much gas and dust in the way, but luckily the modern science of radio astronomy has come to our rescue, since radio waves can penetrate the interstellar matter and give us information about regions which we can never glimpse. To professional astronomers this is one of the most fascinating parts of the whole sky, and and the naked-eye observer can at least appreciate the beauty of it. Keen-eyed watchers may also be able to make out the misty speck which marks the Lagoon Nebula, No. 8 in Messier's list. It is a tremendous gas-cloud, of the same type as the Orion Nebula, and is a spectacular object when seen through a telescope, though its low altitude makes it difficult to see from Britain without optical aid.

CORONA AUSTRALIS: *The Southern Crown*

Abutting on Sagittarius and the sting of Scorpio lies the small constellation Carona Australis, made up of a curved line of faint stars. It is never seen in Britain, but from the southern United States it may be seen without difficulty. It contains nothing of note.

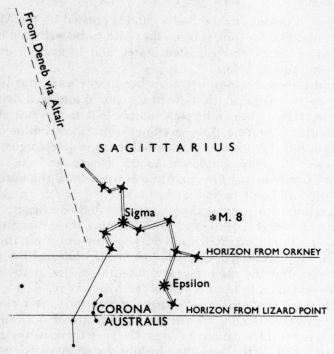

Fig. 60. Sagittarius and Corona Australis.

LIBRA: *The Balance*

The last of the summer groups is Libra, which is a Zodiacal constellation but is otherwise undistinguished. It is at its highest during evenings in July, but it is too faint and too vague to be easily identified.

One way is to continue the main curve of Scorpio, as shown in the diagram. After a while you will reach Alpha Libræ (2·8), after which you should be able to recognize the rest of the group, made up of a quadrilateral of stars. Incidentally, all four have barbarous proper names which have mercifully fallen into disuse. Alpha is Zubenelgenubi, Beta is Zubenelchemali, Gamma is Zubenelhakrabi and Sigma is Zubenalgubi (!). Sigma is of passing interest because it is common to Libra and Scorpio, a reminder that in its original form Libra represented the Scorpion's Claws.

Beta Libræ (2·6) is said to be the only naked-eye star to

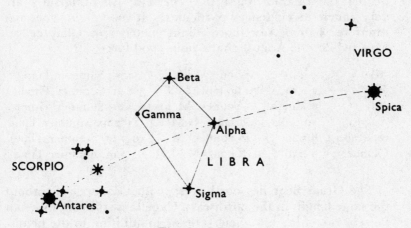

Fig. 61. Libra.

show a distinctly greenish hue. I admit that I have never been able to see the green colour distinctly, but at any rate Beta is worth more than a casual glance. To find it, look between Antares and Arcturus, rather closer to Antares and somewhat west of the connecting line. The method is rough and ready, but it should prove adequate.

By mid-July the evenings are starting to become noticeably darker, and this is probably the best time to look for Scorpio and other bright southern groups, since they become visible at what is usually regarded as "a reasonable hour". They are certainly spectacular, and more than compensate for the large, dull areas occupied by Hercules and his neighbours.

Chapter Thirteen

THE STARS OF AUGUST

AUGUST CAN BE a spectacular month so far as the night sky is concerned. It marks the main meteor shower of the year, and during the first fortnight the "Perseid" shooting-stars are very much in evidence, particularly if moonlight does not interfere. I shall say more about meteors in Chapter 21. Meanwhile, the August charts hold good for:

May 1	4 a.m.	(4 hours G.M.T.)	(5 a.m. Summer Time)
June 1	2 a.m.	(2 hours G.M.T.)	(3 a.m. Summer Time)
July 1	midnight	(0 hours G.M.T.)	(1 a.m. Summer Time)
August 1	10 p.m.	(22 hours G.M.T.)	(11 p.m. Summer Time)
September 1	8 p.m.	(20 hours G.M.T.)	(9 p.m. Summer Time)
October 1	6 p.m.	(18 hours G.M.T.)	(7 p.m. Summer Time)

The Great Bear lies north-west, with Cassiopeia at about the same height in the north-east. Capella is still very low, but Perseus is coming into view. The main addition to the hemispherical charts is the Square of Pegasus, characteristic of the autumn—still not far above the horizon, but becoming prominent during the early morning.

Pegasus will provide our autumn "anchor", so for the moment it is enough to say that two of the stars in the W of Cassiopeia point toward it. From the Square, the line of stars marking Andromeda extends down to Perseus, and ultimately to Capella.

Vega is still practically overhead, and the summer triangle of Vega, Altair and Deneb is dominant. Arcturus is dropping in the west, but remains conspicuous, while the formless Hercules, Ophiuchus and Serpens take up much of the southern aspect. Antares is past its best, and Libra has virtually disappeared, though the stars of Sagittarius still make a reasonable display above the southern horizon.

Some more large, dull constellations are coming into view below Aquila and Pegasus. In particular there are Capricornus

134

NORTHERN ASPECT

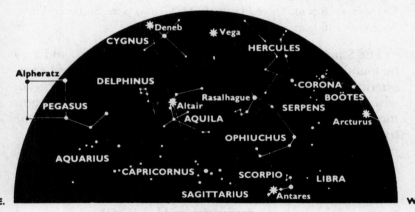

SOUTHERN ASPECT

(the Sea-Goat) and Aquarius (the Water-Carrier), both of which lie in the Zodiac but have nothing else to recommend them.

With darker nights, there is more chance of seeing the Milky Way, and during August evenings the luminous band is high up, passing from Capella through Perseus, Cassiopeia Cygnus, Aquila and down to Sagittarius. The famous branching of the Milky Way in Cygnus is very obvious.

Chapter Fourteen

THE STARS OF SEPTEMBER

THE CHARTS FOR September evenings show one significant feature. Low in the east may be seen the faint shimmer of the Pleiades, the finest open cluster in the sky. I always feel that the appearance of the Pleiades before midnight marks the approach of autumn, and that the period of snowstorms, icy roads, fogs and frozen pipes lies not so very far ahead.

The charts apply to the following times:

June 1	4 a.m.	(4 hours G.M.T.)	(5 a.m. Summer Time)
July 1	2 a.m.	(2 hours G.M.T.)	(3 a.m. Summer Time)
August 1	midnight	(0 hours G.M.T.)	(1 a.m. Summer Time)
September 1	10 p.m.	(22 hours G.M.T.)	(11 p.m. Summer Time)
October 1	8 p.m.	(20 hours G.M.T.)	(9 p.m. Summer Time)
November 1	6 p.m.	(18 hours G.M.T.)	

The Square of Pegasus is high up in the south-east, and may be found by using Cassiopeia as a pointer, though the hemispherical maps do not show this well. Deneb is almost overhead, with Vega beginning to drop westward; Altair remains prominent, but Antares has set. Part of Sagittarius can still be seen, and Ophiuchus and Serpens take up much of the area near the western horizon, though their relative dimness means that any appreciable mist will hide them. Hercules is no brighter, but it is at least higher up.

In the northern aspect, the Great Bear is comparatively low down, while Arcturus is barely visible. Capella has gained enough altitude to be really prominent—and, of course, the Pleiades cluster has made its entry, even though Aldebaran, leader of the Bull, is still invisible.

One other first-magnitude star is on view. Well below the Square of Pegasus, very low down as seen from England, lies Fomalhaut in the otherwise unremarkable constellation of Piscis Austrinus (the Southern Fish). Fomalhaut is really quite bright; it equals Pollux, senior of the Twins, and surpasses Deneb, but it is never well seen from British latitudes,

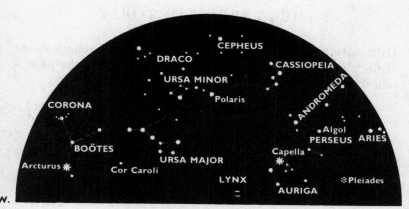

NORTHERN ASPECT

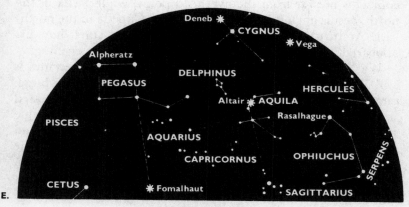

SOUTHERN ASPECT

and from North Scotland it scarcely rises at all. I remember that when I first saw it to advantage—from the island of Madeira, off the African coast—I was decidedly impressed by it; observers in Britain tend to underrate it, which is natural enough in consideration of its unfavourable altitude.

Chapter Fifteen

THE STARS OF OCTOBER

DURING OCTOBER EVENINGS, the autumn constellations are at their best. First, let us give the times for which the hemispherical maps have been drawn:

July 1	4 a.m.	(4 hours G.M.T.	(5 a.m. Summer Time)
August 1	2 a.m.	(2 hours G.M.T.	(3 a.m. Summer Time)
September 1	midnight	(0 hours G.M.T.	(1 a.m. Summer Time)
October 1	10 p.m.	(22 hours G.M.T.)	(11 p.m. Summer Time)
November 1	8 p.m.	(20 hours G.M.T.)	
December 1	6 p.m.	(18 hours G.M.T.)	

The Great Bear is to all intents and purposes at its lowest in the north, still reasonably high up from Britain, extremely near the horizon in the mid-United States. Cassiopeia, of course, is not far from the overhead point, while Vega in the north-west is not a great deal higher than Capella in the north-east. Arcturus, third of the brilliant northern stars, has disappeared, since during October it sets early in the evening.

We have also lost part of Ophiuchus, though Hercules is still above the horizon. To replace Ophiuchus, another large, dim group—Cetus, the Whale or Sea-Monster—has appeared in the south-east. Much more striking is Taurus, now visible in its entirety. The Summer Triangle of Vega, Deneb and Altair remains prominent, with Deneb very high up. The Milky Way too is finely displayed, and passes over the zenith.

The southern aspect is dominated by Pegasus, which has appeared on our charts before.

PEGASUS: *The Flying Horse*

On maps, Pegasus looks extremely conspicuous. Its four main stars make up a square, and it might be thought that they would stand out at once. In point of fact, they do not—partly because they are not really bright, and partly because the Square is very large. Once found, it will be recognized

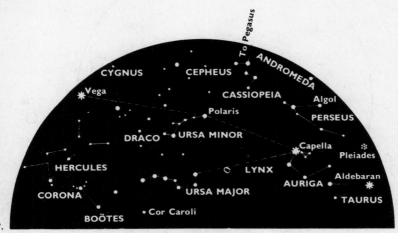

NORTHERN ASPECT

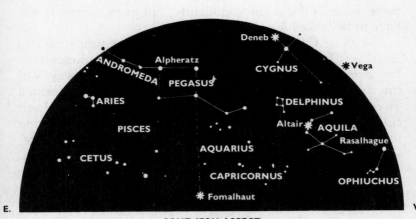

SOUTHERN ASPECT

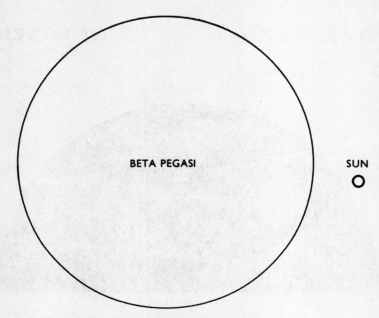

BETA PEGASI

SUN

Fig. 62. Size of Beta Pegasi compared with the Sun.

again without the slightest difficulty, but at the outset it will have to be looked for carefully.

The W of Cassiopeia makes a good pointer, since the two variables Gamma and Alpha act as direction indicators. A line passed through them, and continued for some way, will run straight to Pegasus. Also, look for the arrangement which gives the Pegasus group a vague resemblance to a distorted and enlarged Plough. From the Square, the line of stars marking the neighbouring group, Andromeda, extends across to Capella, while the brightest star in Perseus fits into the general pattern.

The brightest member of the Square is often known by its Arabic name of Alpheratz. For some unknown reason it has been transferred away from Pegasus, and is now officially termed Alpha Andromedæ, so providing a typical example of the illogical parcelling-out of the stars. Its magnitude is 2·1, so that it almost equals Polaris. The other Square stars are fainter; Alpha Pegasi (2·5), Gamma (2·8) and Beta, a variable fluctuating more or less irregularly between $2\frac{1}{4}$ and $2\frac{3}{4}$. Gamma, the lower left-hand star, is not much above the third magnitude, and when there is considerably low-lying haze it may well be hidden, so giving the Square an incomplete appearance. However, this will not usually be the case during October evenings, when the Square is high in the sky and well clear of horizon mist.

The most notable star in the constellation is Beta, a vast, cool Red Giant. It is more than 200 light-years away, and has a diameter of some 150,000,000 miles, but like all its kind it is very rarefied; its mass is only nine times that of the Sun. Fig. 62 shows the two stars drawn to the same scale. The difference in size is tremendous, and yet it would take only nine Suns to balance the huge globe of Beta Pegasi. The star's outer layers, at least, are very much less dense than the air we breathe.

Beta Pegasi is not so luminous as Betelgeux in Orion, but it is of the same type; its official magnitude range is given as 2·4 to 2·7, but there are suggestions that the true range may be greater than this. There is a very rough period of between 35 and 40 days, but one can never tell quite how Beta is going to behave. Alpha and Gamma make good comparisons stars, but the observer must always remember to allow for extinction (see page 246). Seen from northern latitudes, Beta is always much higher than Gamma or Alpha.

The Square provides a good opportunity of showing how uncrowded the sky really is. The area covered is large, but not very many faint stars can be seen inside it without optical aid; anyone who counts a dozen is doing well, though really keen-eyed people will glimpse more.

The only other important star in Pegasus is Epsilon (2·3), which is well away from the Square, and is in a relatively isolated position between Alpha Pegasi and Altair. It has been thought to be slightly variable, and is worth watching. Binoculars show that it is decidedly orange.

In mythology, Pegasus was the wonderful flying horse upon which the hero Bellerophon rode in order to kill a fire-breathing monster of notoriously peevish disposition. There is little about the celestial Pegasus to conjure up the picture of a horse, flying or otherwise, but at least the well-marked Square is a dominating feature of autumn skies.

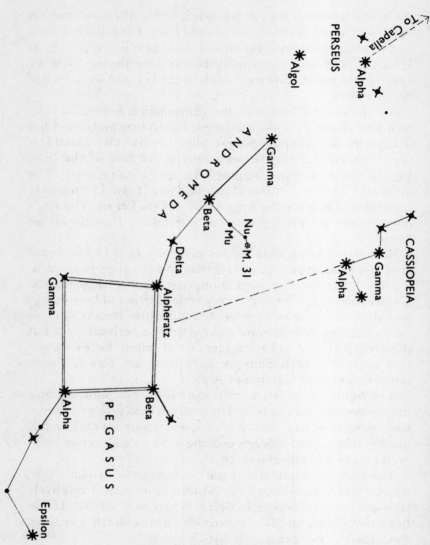

Fig. 63. Pegasus and Andromeda.

ANDROMEDA

Linked with Pegasus is Andromeda, the princess of the legend in which Perseus, Cassiopeia, Cepheus and Cetus play the other leading rôles. Needless to say, the pattern is nothing like a princess; Andromeda's chief stars are arranged in a somewhat irregular line running from the Square toward Perseus. In order, they are Alpha or Alpheratz (2·1), Delta (3·2), Beta (2·0) and Gamma (2·1).

There is an interesting colour-contrast here. Alpheratz is white and Gamma slightly orange, while Beta is definitely orange-red. In fact, the hue of Beta is the same as that of Betelgeux, though since the star is a magnitude fainter its colour is not so evident to the naked eye. It is a Red Giant, but there is no positive evidence that it is variable. If it fluctuates at all, the magnitude-range is extremely slight.

Andromeda is celebrated because it includes one object of unique interest: the Great Spiral, formerly but misleadingly known as the Great Nebula. It was No. 31 in Messier's catalogue, and has been familiar to sky-watchers for a very long time, but only during our own century was it proved to be a separate galaxy far beyond the limits of the star-system in which we live. But for the Great Spiral, our knowledge of the nature of the universe might still be somewhat limited. It is the only really large external galaxy near enough to be studied in detail.

It is definitely visible to the naked eye, though clear, dark skies are needed; street lamps will drown it, and so will any hint of haze. To locate it, first find Beta Andromedæ, which is easy enough. Then look upward; you will see two fainter stars, Mu (3·9) and Nu (4·4). The Spiral lies close to Nu, slightly to the "right-hand side".

It cannot be said that the Spiral is spectacular with the naked eye, and the casual observer will be lucky to see it at all. Neither, for that matter, is it well seen in a small or moderate telescope, as it looks like a dim blur of light. Yet it is immensely significant. Photographs taken with giant instruments show that it is starry in nature, and that its form is truly like that of a Catherine-wheel, though since it lies at an angle to us the spiral effect is rather spoiled.

Until after the first German war, it was not known whether the Andromeda Spiral and other "starry nebulæ" were true members of our own Galaxy. Then, in 1923, the American astronomer E. E. Hubble found some Cepheids in the Spiral.

Cepheid has been studied, and its period measured,
can be worked out, and Hubble realized at once
ral must be an external system. Modern estimates
,200,000 light-years from us, so that we are now
used to be before men appeared on Earth. Even
f the very closest of the outer galaxies.

It has been found, too, that the Spiral is appreciably larger
than our own Galaxy. It contains objects of all kinds, ranging
from giant stars to clusters, gaseous nebulæ, novæ and occasional supernovæ; it also emits long-wavelength radiations
which have been picked up by instruments such as the large
radio telescope at Jodrell Bank, near Manchester.

Most of the outer galaxies are racing away from us at high
speeds, but astronomers have found that our Galaxy, the
Andromeda Spiral, the fainter spiral in the constellation of
Triangulum, the two southern Clouds of Magellan, and various
smaller systems make up what is called the Local Group,
whose members are not receding. In this Local Group, the
Andromeda Spiral is unquestionably the senior member, with
our Galaxy taking second place.

I have already pointed out that the Andromeda Spiral is the
remotest object visible with the naked eye. The proper answer
to the question "How far can you see without a telescope?" is
"2·2 million light-years." If the Earth-Sun distance is scaled
down to one inch, the Spiral will be over two million miles off.

No other spirals can be seen without a telescope, and for this
reason alone it is always fascinating to go out on a dark night
and locate Messier 31, the dim, hazy patch which has proved
to be a colossal system of well over one hundred thousand
million suns.

ARIES: *The Ram*

Aries is famous as being the first constellation of the Zodiac.
The point known as the Vernal Equinox, where the Sun's
yearly path among the stars cuts the celestial equator, used to
lie here. Though the slight shifting of the Earth's axis has now
moved the vernal equinox out of Aries into the adjacent
constellation of Pisces, the term "First Point of Aries" is still
used.

Alpha (2·0), the leader of Aries, may be found rather south

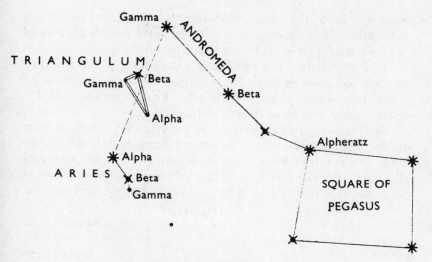

Fig. 64. Aries and Triangulum.

of the Andromeda chain. It is rather isolated, and there should be no difficulty in recognizing it; during October evenings it is high in the sky. It is orange in hue, though to the naked eye it will probably look white. There are two more stars of reasonable brilliancy, Beta (2·7) and Gamma (4·0). Gamma is a fine binary, but since it appears single to the naked-eye observer it need not concern us at present.

TRIANGULUM: *The Triangle*

It is unusual to find a constellation which looks in the least like the object which it is named. Triangulum is the exception, since its three main stars, Beta (3·1), Alpha (3·6) and Gamma (4·1) are indeed arranged in a triangle. The group lies between Alpha Arietis and Gamma Andromedæ, but is of no immediate interest, since its only notable feature—the spiral galaxy Messier 33—is below naked-eye visibility. Some people claim to have glimpsed it, but personally I have grave doubts!

PISCES: *The Fishes*

Pisces may be termed "the Last and the First"; it used to be the twelfth and last constellation of the Zodiac, but owing to the shift of the vernal equinox it has now become the first. The

Sun lies in Pisces around March 22, when it crosses the celestial equator moving from south to north; this is the official beginning of spring in the northern hemisphere.

During October evenings Pisces is high up, but it is not easy to find, because its stars are so faint. Even the brightest of them, Eta, is only of magnitude 3·7. The best way to find it is to use Alpha and Beta Arietis as pointers.

The main constellation is made up of a long string of stars below Andromeda and the Square of Pegasus. If you connect Beta and Gamma Pegasi, and continue the line for an equal distance, you will arrive in the middle of Pisces, and it should be possible to identify the group at once, but there is nothing

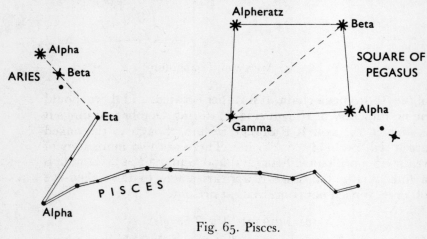

Fig. 65. Pisces.

of interest to be seen. The Pisces chain ends below Alpha Pegasi in the Square.

PISCIS AUSTRINUS: *The Southern Fish*

The region above the southern horizon during October evenings is, on the whole, remarkably barren, but it does contin one bright star. This is Fomalhaut, in the constellation sometimes known as Piscis Austrinus and sometimes (less accurately) as Piscis Australis.

Fomalhaut is of magnitude 1·2, so that it is about equal to Pollux and definitely brighter than Regulus. It is never well seen from Europe or the northern United States, but luckily

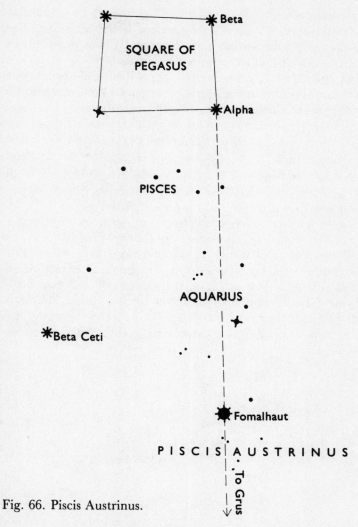

Fig. 66. Piscis Austrinus.

Beta and Alpha in Pegasus give a perfect guide-line to it; the
pointer passes across a dim region so that Fomalhaut is the
first bright star to be reached. Actually, the best time to look
is about 8 to 9 p.m. (9 to 10 p.m. Summer Time) in mid-
October; by midnight the star will have to all intents and
purposes disappeared, though from the latitude of New York
it is higher up and is observable for longer.

Fomalhaut is white. It is a mere 23 light-years away, so that apart from Sirius, Procyon and Altair it is the nearest of the first-magnitude stars visible from Europe. It is as powerful as 13 Suns, or about half as luminous as Sirius.

Piscis Austrinus is one of the original constellations, but apart from Fomalhaut it is entirely unremarkable, since there is no other star as bright as the fourth magnitude.

GRUS: *The Crane*

Grus, the brightest of the four "Southern Birds", is invisible from Britain, and most of it is always too low to be seen from the New York area. Go down to Florida, or to North Africa, and you will find it shining quite prominently.

The best pointer to use is the line starting from the Square of Pegasus and passing through Fomalhaut. This leads on to the two main stars of Grus, Alpha (1·8) and Beta (2·2). The line of fainter stars extending in the general direction of Capricornus does give a vague impression of a flying bird. Adjoining Grus to the east is another bird, Phœnix. There is one fairly bright star—Alpha (2·4)—but there is nothing else of note, and since Phœnix cannot be seen from Europe or

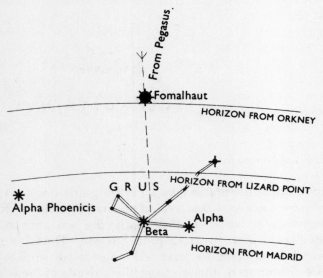

Fig. 67. Grus.

most of the United States there seems no reason to dwell upon it here.

CETUS: *The Whale*

Cetus is yet another large constellation with few bright stars, but it is not hard to identify its leader, Beta (2·0); the method is to go back to the Square of Pegasus, and use Alpheratz and Gamma Pegasi as pointers. The lining-up is not exact, but it is quite good enough, since Beta Ceti is decidedly isolated. The only possible confusion is with Fomalhaut, which is further west, considerably lower and almost a magnitude brighter.

Orion can also be pressed into service, the guide-stars here being Betelgeux and Bellatrix. However, the distance to be covered is inconveniently great, and of course Orion is not shown on our October charts. Early in the month, the celestial hunter does not appear properly until after midnight.

Having located Beta, at one end of Cetus, the next step is to find the whale's head, at the other end of the constellation. For this, Beta Andromedæ and Alpha Arietis may be used. The head is marked by four stars making up a quadrilateral; the brightest, Alpha (2·5) is orange, though the light level is too low for the colour to be at all obvious with the naked eye.

So far as the rest of Cetus is concerned, the only way to make it out is to identify the head (Alpha) and the tail (Beta), and then check the rest of the stars shown on the map. It is worth finding Tau (3·5), which is only about 12 light-years away, and was one of the two stars studied by radio astronomers a few years ago in the forlorn hope of detecting artificial signals —since it was thought possible that Tau Ceti, a star rather cooler and fainter than our Sun, might be the centre of a system of planets. (The other star to receive attention during this programme was Epsilon Eridani, described on page 80.) However, much the most intriguing object in Cetus is the red long-period variable Omicron, better known by its proper name of Mira, "The Wonderful Star".

Mira has a long history. It was seen by the Dutch astronomer Fabricius in 1596, and recorded as being of the third magnitude, but a few weeks later it could no longer be found. Bayer, the German observer who first gave the stars their Greek

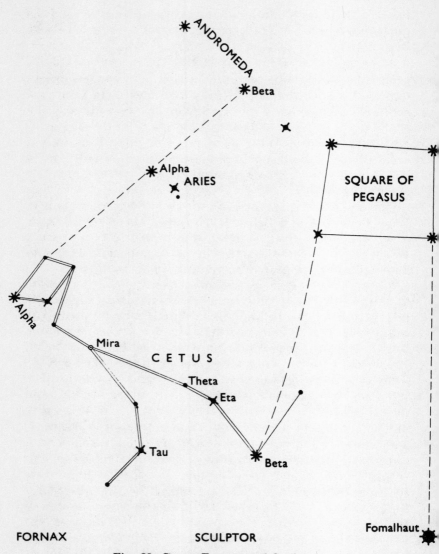

Fig. 68. Cetus, Fornax and Sculptor.

letters, saw it again in 1603, but again it vanished after a week or two. Later, it was established that Mira appears and disappears with fair regularity. It has a period of about 331 days; at its best it may equal Polaris, but when near minimum it fades down to the ninth magnitude, so that it is beyond the range of the naked-eye observer and cannot be seen even with binoculars.

Mira is quite different from the regular-as-clockwork short-period variables such as Delta Cephei. Its period is not precise, and the interval between successive maxima may not be exactly 331 days. Moreover, some maxima are brighter than others; in 1868, for instance, the star never exceeded the fourth magnitude.

Generally, Mira is visible with the naked eye for about 18 weeks of its full period, but sometimes it remains on view for over 20 weeks, whereas in 1868 its appearance was limited to 12 weeks. Even this sounds more encouraging than it really is, because for part of this "visible period" it is too dim to be identified except by an observer who knows every faint star in the area. And to make matters still worse, maximum may occur at a time when the star is above the horizon only during daylight. Only when maximum takes place during the autumn or early winter is it possible to follow Mira without a telescope.

Here again we are dealing with a vast Red Giant, of tremendous size but low density. There is a roughly regular pulsation; as the star swells out and subsequently contracts, the energy output changes and the light varies. We cannot pretend to know the full causes of this behaviour, but at any rate Mira is not unique. It is typical of a whole class of long-period variables, thousands of which are now known. Mira is the brightest of its kind, and, at its distance of 103 light-years, is also the nearest to us.

A special identification chart for Mira is given on page 233. For the moment, it is enough to say that it lies not very far from the Whale's head, so that it should be recognizable if it is bright enough to be seen with the naked eye even though its redness is not obvious without optical aid. Yearly almanacs give its dates of maxima, and although these dates cannot be forecast accurately they should be good enough to indicate whether Mira is likely to be visible or not.

When Mira becomes unusually conspicuous it can cause excitement among observers who are not familiar with it. On numerous occasions it has been mistaken for a nova. The beginner who sees an unexpected bright star near Cetus' head would be wise to have second thoughts before making a sensational announcement!

Mythologically, Cetus has been identified with the sea-monster which was sent to gobble up the Princess Andromeda, and was summarily turned to stone when Perseus showed it the Gorgon's head. More recently, however, it seems to have become a harmless whale. There are a few more stars brighter than the fourth magnitude, but only Mira is really of interest to the naked-eye observer.

FORNAX: *The Furnace* and SCULPTOR: *The Sculptor*

For the sake of completeness, mention should be made of two very obscure groups adjoining Cetus. These are Fornax and Sculptor, both added to the sky by the French astronomer Lacaille in 1752, and originally known as Fornax Chemica (the Chemical Furnace) and Apparatus Sculptoris (the Sculptor's Apparatus). Both are very low as seen from northern countries, and both are devoid of bright stars or interesting objects, so that I have merely indicated their positions on the map given for Cetus.

CAPRICORNUS: *The Sea-Goat*

The idea of a marine goat may seem rather peculiar, but in some legends the Zodiacal constellation of Capricornus is identified with the pastoral demigod Pan. There is only one notable object, the naked-eye double Alpha. The brightest star is Delta (2·9).

The best way to locate Capricornus is to start with Altair in Aquila. The line of three stars of which Altair is the central member points straight down to the Sea-Goat, arriving at Alpha, which is made up of two components of magnitudes 3·8 and 4·5 respectively. Both may be seen easily enough, since the distance between them amounts to 376 seconds of arc. Nearby lies the rather brighter star Beta (3·1); this also is double, but the components are too close to be separated with the naked eye.

MICROSCOPIUM: *The Microscope*

Below Capricornus lies a small, faint constellation whose name, Microscopium, shows that it is a relatively modern

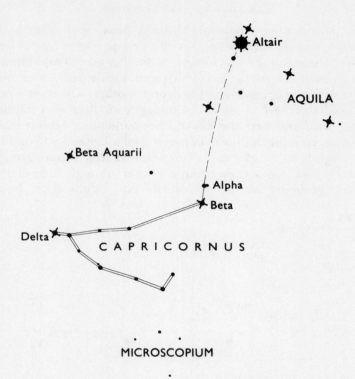

Fig. 69. Capricornus and Microscopium.

addition to the sky. Like Fornax and Sculptor, it was first drawn by Lacaille in 1752. Most of it rises from Britain, and all of it clears the horizon from New York, but it is entirely uninteresting.

AQUARIUS: *The Water-Bearer*

In our description of the constellations visible from northern lands we come finally to Aquarius, the "Man with the Watering-Pot". We are ending on a subdued note, since although Aquarius is in the Zodiac, and is one of the ancient groups, it is formless and faint.

Again the Square of Pegasus gives us a guide. A line from Alpheratz, passed through Alpha Pegasi and continued for a somewhat greater distance beyond, will arrive at the third-magnitude star Alpha Aquarii (3·0), one of a quartet arranged in an irregular line. Beyond Alpha is Beta (2·9). The only other reasonably bright star in the group, Delta (3·3), lies more or less along the line joining Alpha Pegasi to Fomalhaut.

In point of fact Aquarius spreads over a wide area, touching Capricornus on one side and Cetus on the other. The direction-line used to find Fomalhaut, running from Beta and Alpha Pegasi, will cross first the tail of Pisces and then extend into Aquarius. Roughly half-way between Alpha Pegasi and Fomalhaut, slightly to the east of the line, may be seen a small group of stars which looks rather like a cluster, though it is not a genuine grouping and is not of any real significance. It is

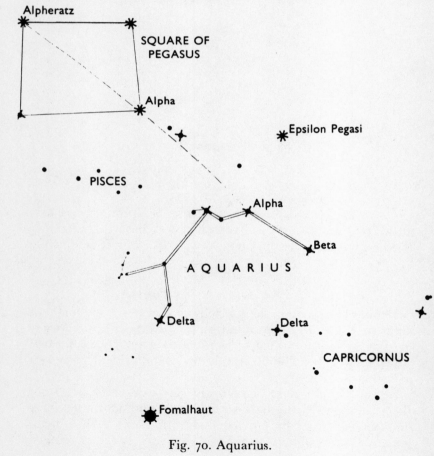

Fig. 70. Aquarius.

worth looking at with binoculars, since several of the stars in the pattern are orange in colour.

All things considered, the area including Capricornus, Aquarius, Pisces and Cetus is one of the most barren parts of the sky. The best that can be said for it is that it is less confusing than the Ophiuchus area, and that since part of it lies in the Zodiac it is sometimes graced by a brilliant planet. During the autumn of 1964, for instance, Saturn lay in Aquarius and Jupiter in Pisces. Should you see a really bright object in that region, you may be sure that it is a planet; of the stars, only Fomalhaut aspires to any eminence.

Chapter Sixteen

THE STARS OF NOVEMBER

THE NOVEMBER CHARTS re-introduce a familiar and brilliant constellation: Orion is visible once more, though it does not come into full view much before midnight. The charts apply to:

August 1	4 a.m.	(4 hours G.M.T.)	(5 a.m. Summer Time)
September 1	2 a.m.	(2 hours G.M.T.)	(3 a.m. Summer Time)
October 1	midnight	(0 hours G.M.T.)	(1 a.m. Summer Time)
November 1	10 p.m.	(22 hours G.M.T.)	
December 1	8 p.m.	(20 hours G.M.T.)	
January 1	6 p.m.	(18 hours G.M.T.)	

Orion is not yet high enough to be used as a general guide, but at least Aldebaran and the Pleiades have become prominent, while Castor and Pollux are rising in the east. The Summer Triangle has lost its dominance; Vega and Deneb are still conspicuous, but Altair has become low in the west. Capricornus has gone, and Fomalhaut is very low down, though Aquarius is still to be seen.

Pegasus is in the high south, somewhat west of the meridian; the Andromeda line leads to Alpha Persei, which is not far from the zenith. Cassiopeia, too, is at its greatest altitude, while the Great Bear has reached its lowest. Arcturus, of course, is invisible. If you want to see Arcturus on a night in November, you must wait until about 4 a.m.

The Milky Way passes through the overhead point during the late evening, and on a clear, frosty night it is a superb spectacle. It is worth noting, though, that a night of this sort is not always of much use to the observer with a telescope; when the air is very transparent, and the stars are twinkling violently, it is fairly safe to assume that conditions will be unsteady, so that an object such as a planet will wobble about

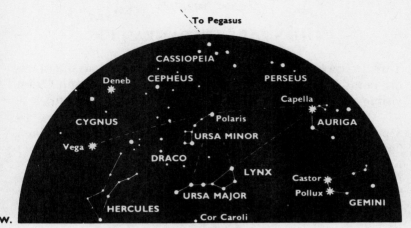

NORTHERN ASPECT

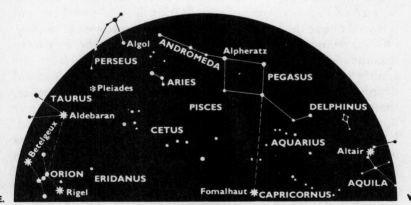

SOUTHERN ASPECT

as though being viewed through several layers of water. Yet this does not affect the casual watcher. So far as he is concerned, clarity is the essential factor; and during a November night, it is often possible to see stars which are normally at the very limit of naked-eye visibility.

Chapter Seventeen

THE STARS OF DECEMBER

THE DECEMBER CHARTS bring us almost back to our starting-point, with the Great Bear standing on its tail and Orion
visible once more in the south-east. The charts apply to:

September 1 4 a.m.   (4 hours G.M.T.) (5 a.m. Summer Time)
October 1   2 a.m.   (2 hours G.M.T.) (3 a.m. Summer Time)
November 1 midnight (o hours G.M.T.)
December 1 10 p.m.   (22 hours G.M.T.)
January 1   8 p.m.   (20 hours G.M.T.)
February 1 6 p.m.   (18 hours G.M.T.)

All the main guides—Orion, the Bear, Cassiopeia and the
Square of Pegasus—are on view. Orion is not at its best, but
it is well above the horizon, and dominates that area of the sky.
Of its retinue. Sirius is barely visible, but all the rest have
become conspicuous. Capella has not arrived back at the
zenith, but is very high up, and cannot be mistaken; Vega has
dropped almost out of sight, and Altair has gone altogether,
though Deneb is still to be seen. Delphinus remains above the
horizon, but is not likely to be seen unless deliberately sought.
I mention it here only because I once had a letter from a
newcomer to astronomy who had caught sight of Delphinus on
a December evening, and had mixed it up with the Pleiades.

Perseus is high, so that this is a good period to follow the
strange winkings of the Demon Star, Algol. Cetus, too, is
visible for most of the night; should Mira reach its maximum
toward the end of the year, it should be easily recognized. The
Milky Way makes a fine showing, stretching from Cygnus in
the north-west right across the sky to Monoceros in the south-
east. Leo has not fully appeared, but makes its entry in the
east during the early hours of a December morning, so that
it is high in the sky well before sunrise.

While talking about the December stars, something ought

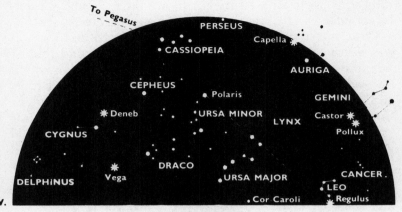

NORTHERN ASPECT

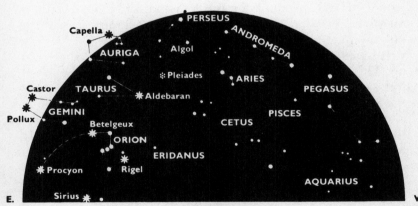

SOUTHERN ASPECT

perhaps to be said about the famous Star of Bethlehem, described in the Bible. Many people have wondered what it can have been. The favourite candidates are Venus, Jupiter and Sirius, but actually "the Star in the East" can have been none of these. If the Biblical account is correct, the object must have been unusual; had it been a normal star or planet, the Three Wise Men would not have given it a second thought.

There is little information to guide us, since the Star is

mentioned only once in the Bible. We rely entirely upon St. Matthew; the other Gospels are completely silent on the subject. Neither are we sure about our dates, though we may be confident that Christ was not born on December 25, A.D.1.

C. L. Ideler, a last-century German, believed that the Star was due to the planets Jupiter and Saturn, shining side by side and giving the impression of one mass. Unfortunately it has since been shown that Ideler's calculations were wrong, and the whole idea must be ruled out of court. Halley's Comet has also been suggested, and was at perihelion in the year 11 B.C., so that with regard to the time scale it would just about fit. A nova or supernova is another possibility, but in this case why do no contemporary scientific accounts mention it? My own idea, put forward some years ago, is that the Star of Bethlehem was the result of a garbled description of two meteors which appeared at different times, moving in the same direction. The explanation may sound weak, but it would at least account for the fact that only St. Matthew mentions the Star, while none of the astronomers of the day say anything about it.

It is very doubtful whether the problem will ever be cleared up. The evidence is hopelessly scanty, and we cannot even tell if the tale is founded on any sort of scientific fact. In any case, the Star of Bethlehem has never been reported since.

This review of the night-sky over a full year is necessarily very incomplete, but if the newcomer cares to take the charts given here, check to see which constellations are visible and which are not, and then follow the method of identifying at least one new group every clear night, it should not take him long to find his way around; in time, the constellations will become recognizable at a glance. The only limitation is that city-dwellers are bound to be in trouble from the outset. Not long ago I stood in Regent's Park, on a late evening in summer, and tried to find the stars. I could see Vega, together with Deneb and Altair, and a few other stars, but that was all. Artificial lights cause a glow in the sky which is more or less fatal, and the only real solution is to go out into the country, where the sky is dark and the air relatively free of smoke and grime.

A NOTE ON STAR NAMES

Modern astronomers shun the old Arabic names of the stars, apart from the "top twenty" or so. However, air and sea navigators still use them to some extent, so that it may be worth giving a few of them. In the following list, I have confined myself to bright or particularly notable stars visible from latitude 50 degrees North.

ANDROMEDA	Alpha:	Alpheratz	LYRA	Alpha:	Vega
	Beta:	Mirach	OPHIUCHUS	Alpha:	Rasalhague
	Gamma:	Almaak	ORION	Alpha:	Betelgeux
AQUILA	Alpha:	Altair		Beta:	Rigel
ARIES	Alpha:	Hamal		Gamma:	Bellatrix
AURIGA	Alpha:	Capella		Delta:	Mintaka
	Beta:	Menkarlina		Epsilon:	Alnilam
BOÖTES	Alpha:	Arcturus		Zeta	Alnitak
CANES VENATICI	Alpha:	Cor Caroli		Kappa:	Saiph
CANIS MAJOR	Alpha:	Sirius	PEGASUS	Alpha:	Markab
	Beta:	Mirzam		Beta:	Scheat
	Delta	Wezea		Gamma:	Algenib
	Epsilon:	Adara		Epsilon:	Enif
CANIS MINOR	Alpha:	Procyon	PERSEUS	Alpha:	Mirphak
CASSIOPEIA	Alpha:	Shedir		Beta:	Algol
CETUS	Alpha:	Menkar	PISCIS AUSTRINUS	Alpha:	Fomalhaut
	Beta:	Diphda	SAGITTARIUS	Sigma:	Nunki
	Omicron:	Mira	SCORPIO	Alpha:	Antares
CORONA BOREALIS	Alpha:	Alphekka	TAURUS	Alpha:	Aldebaran
CYGNUS	Alpha:	Deneb		Beta:	Alnath
	Beta:	Albireo		Eta:	Alcyone
	Gamma:	Sadr	URSA MAJOR	Alpha:	Dubhe
DRACO	Alpha:	Thuban		Beta:	Merak
	Gamma:	Etamin		Gamma:	Phad
GEMINI	Alpha:	Castor		Delta:	Megrez
	Beta:	Pollux		Epsilon:	Alioth
	Gamma:	Alhena		Zeta:	Mizar
HERCULES	Alpha:	Rasalgethi		Eta:	Alkaid
HYDRA	Alpha:	Alphard	URSA MINOR	Alpha:	Polaris
LEO	Alpha:	Regulus		Beta:	Kocab
	Beta:	Denebola	VIRGO	Alpha:	Spica
	Gamma:	Algieba			

Argo   Canopus

Chapter Eighteen

THE PLANETS

AMATEUR ASTRONOMERS, AS a class, tend to give their main attention to our nearest neighbours in space, the members of the Solar System. True, there are a good many enthusiasts who concentrate upon variable stars, but generally speaking the Moon and planets are the amateur's chief hunting-ground.

This means, of course, that a telescope is absolutely essential if useful work is to be done. The naked-eye observer must content himself with recognizing the planets and following their movements against the starry background, which is entertaining even if it leads to no epoch-making scientific discoveries. Fortunately, four of the planets—Venus, Mars, Jupiter and Saturn—are extremely bright, while Mercury may be seen without optical aid when best placed, and Uranus is at the limit of naked-eye visibility.

Any rough scale map of the Solar System shows that the planets are divided up into two groups. The inner group consists of four relatively small, solid worlds: Mercury, Venus, the Earth and Mars. Then comes a wide gap, filled by thousands of dwarf bodies known variously as planetoids, asteroids and minor planets; only one of them can ever be seen without a telescope, and even the largest is below 500 miles in diameter. Beyond the asteroid belt come the four giants, Jupiter, Saturn, Uranus and Neptune, while the frontier of the planetary system is marked by strange little Pluto, which is too faint to be seen without a telescope of fair size and which has set astronomers any number of problems since it was discovered in 1930. Planets may, of course, be photographed with an ordinary camera, as shown in Plates V*b* and VI.

Mercury and Venus, which are closer to the Sun than we are, have their own way of behaving. Obviously they will always lie in roughly the same direction as the Sun, as is shown by the diagram in Fig. 71. For the moment we may regard the Earth as stationary, with Mercury moving round the Sun at a mean distance of 36 million miles and Venus at

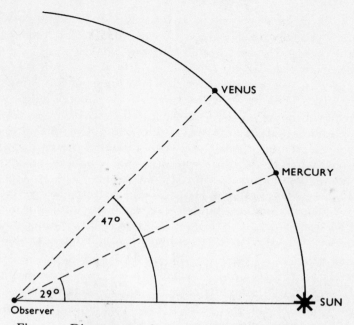

Fig. 71. Diagram to show that Mercury and Venus always appear in much the same general direction as the Sun.

67 million miles (the Earth-Sun distance is, of course, 93 million miles). The apparent angle between Venus and the Sun can never be more than 47 degrees, while for Mercury the maximum is less than 30 degrees. This means that neither Mercury nor Venus can remain visible all through the night. They will be confined to the western part of the sky after sunset, or the eastern sky before dawn.

Mercury is not particularly easy to see without a telescope, and under the circumstances it is rather surprising that the ancient star-gazers should have known about it—though admittedly it is much less elusive from Mediterranean countries, with their clear air, than from more northern lands. It has a diameter of about 2,900 miles, which is not a great deal more than that of the Moon, and it never comes much within 50 million miles of us, so that even large instruments will not show fine details upon its surface.

Mercury's "year", or time taken to go once round the Sun,

is 88 Earth-days, so that it is a rapid mover; it is easy to understand why it was named after the fleet-footed Messenger of the Gods. Its nearness to the Sun makes matters very difficult for the naked-eye watcher, and I very much doubt whether an observer who lives close to a town will see Mercury at all; the general sky-glow caused by artificial lights will drown it. From my home in Sussex, well away from any city, I have found that Mercury is visible without optical aid on about a dozen occasions every year, though I remember that in 1963, when the weather was particularly bad at the wrong moments, I failed to see it even once.

The most favourable dates for seeing Mercury are given in astronomical almanacs, but a few notes about conditions in the period from 1965 to 1970 may be helpful. The planet ought to be seen for a day or two to either side of the date given here.

In the west, after sunset: 1965 March 21, 1966 March 5, 1967 February 16, 1968 May 24, 1969 May 5, 1970 April 18.
In the east, before dawn: 1965 September 2, 1966 August 16, 1967 July 30, 1968 October 31, 1969 October 14, 1970 September 28.

Binoculars are a great help, the method being to sweep along the horizon, but it is always necessary to guard against looking at the Sun by mistake. It is probably wisest to wait until the Sun has completely vanished.

When Mercury is found, it may seem surprisingly bright, so that one tends to wonder how it can have been overlooked. It looks like a star, and is said to be pinkish, though few people will regard it as anything but white. It can—and usually does —twinkle noticeably, since when visible with the naked eye it is always very low down. The only hope of seeing it is to catch it immediately after sunset.

Mercury is a peculiar world. It is to all intents and purposes without atmosphere; it is certainly sterile, and as hostile to life as could be imagined. Moreover, it probably keeps the same face toward the Sun all the time, so that it is scorching hot on one side and intensely cold on the other, though recent work casts a certain amount of doubt on the matter, and it has been suggested that the real rotation period may be about two months.

Venus, almost the same size of the Earth, is completely different. It has a high albedo or reflecting power, and sends back over 60% of the sunlight which falls upon it. Since it is also our nearest neighbour apart from the Moon, and may approach us to within 25 million miles, it is remarkably bright. It far outshines any other star or planet, and may attain magnitude $-4\frac{1}{2}$, so that it is capable of casting shadows. Unlike Mercury, it may set over five hours after the Sun or rise five hours before the Sun, so that it is often visible against a dark background.

There can be no trouble about recognizing Venus, because of its extreme brilliance; even Jupiter cannot match it, and so far as the naked-eye observer is concerned Venus is the supreme beauty of the heavens. Telescopically it is a disappointment, because its surface is permanently hidden by its dense atmosphere. Various attempts have been made to find out what surface conditions there are like, but the results are hopelessly contradictory, and all we can really say at the moment is that advanced life-forms are probably absent.

Owners of good binoculars will be able to see that Venus shows phases, or apparent changes of shape, similar to those of the Moon. The reason is not far to seek. Venus, like the other planets, has no light of its own, and depends entirely upon reflecting the rays of the Sun. Only one half of the globe can be illuminated at any one moment; the other half is dark, and so cannot be seen.

In the diagram (Fig. 72), we may again regard the Earth as fixed. At inferior conjunction (1), Venus is almost in front of the Sun, so that its dark side faces us, and the planet is "new". As it moves toward (2) it starts to become visible, first as a crescent and then as a half; when it reaches (2) it is at its greatest elongation west of the Sun, and is a morning star. It then becomes gibbous, or threequarter phase, and at position (3), or superior conjunction, it is full—though since it is almost behind the Sun it is invisible to the naked eye, and is difficult to follow even with an accurate telescope. It then starts to wane, returning to a half-shape at eastern elongation (4) as an evening star. Subsequently it becomes a narrowing crescent before returning to inferior conjunction.

I make no apology for this digression, because it is not

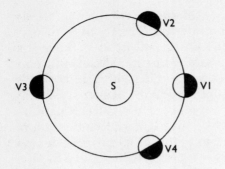

Fig. 72. Phases of Venus.

irrelevant. It has often been claimed that the phase of Venus may be seen with the naked eye, though admittedly only during the crescent stage. Not many people are keen-sighted enough for this, but the favoured few can undoubtedly see the cresent form when conditions are ideal; for instance my old friend Herbert W. Cornell, well-known in America as an amateur astronomer, was able to do so on a single occasion many years ago.

The behaviour of Venus for the 1965–70 period may be summarized quite concisely. Remember that at eastern elongation Venus is at its best as an evening star, while at western elongation it is well placed as a morning star; near inferior or superior conjunction it cannot be seen with the naked eye.

1965. Superior conjunction April 12. Eastern elongation November 15.
1966. Inferior conjunction January 26. Western elongation April 6. Superior conjunction November 9.
1967. Eastern elongation June 20. Inferior conjunction August 29. Western elongation November 9.
1968. Superior conjunction June 20.
1969. Eastern elongation January 26. Inferior conjunction April 8. Western elongation June 17.
1970. Superior conjunction January 24. Eastern elongation September 1. Inferior conjunction November 10.

Thus throughout the autumn and early winter of 1965–66, Venus is a brilliant object in the west after sunset. From the data given here, it is easy to work out just when and where Venus will be visible at any particular moment. As a further example, let us take the year 1969. Eastern elongation occurs in late January, and inferior conjunction on April 8, so that for the first part of the year the planet will be an evening star in the west; it will reappear as a morning star in late April, and will be conspicuous in the east before sunrise well into the winter.

Venus is so striking that it may often be seen in broad day-light, with the Sun well above the horizon. Sometimes it comes into view quite unexpectedly, and it seems worth quoting from an account written by the last-century French astronomer Arago. Apparently Napoleon Bonaparte was at-tending an official fête in Luxembourg when he "was very much surprised at seeing the multitude . . . pay more attention to the regions of the heavens situate above the palace than to his person or the brilliant staff which accompanied him. He inquired the cause, and learned that these curious persons were observing with astonishment, although it was noon, a star, which they supposed to be that of the Conqueror of Italy; an allusion to which the illustrious general did not seem indifferent when he himself with his piercing eyes observed the radiant body".

From countries with clear skies, it seems that Venus is not difficult to see in the middle of the day provided that the observer knows where to look for it. Matters are more difficult in Britain, but even here Venus becomes visible well before sunset when suitably placed, while it may also be followed for some time after sunrise during times when it is a morning star.

When Venus shines down from a dark sky, its shadow effects may be quite marked, and it is interesting to experi-ment with a white screen; the shadows are very sharp, since Venus is practically a point source of light. And when the planet is seen shining above the sea or a lake, the "light trail" across the water is really beautiful. I saw this excellently in the late summer of 1964, from Loch Ness in Scotland; the trail stretched right across the loch, though unfortunately it failed to reveal any trace of the famous Monster.

On rare occasions both Venus and Mercury may pass directly in front of the Sun, so showing up in transit as black spots. Transits of Mercury are invisible with the naked eye, and so do not concern us at the moment. Venus is conspicuous when in transit, showing up clearly against the brilliant solar disk, but unfortunately I cannot provide an eye-witness account, since the last transit occurred in 1882. The next will not take place until June 7, 2004.

The other planets lie beyond the Earth's orbit in the Solar System, so that they do not show phases from new to full. (This is obvious enough. To appear as a thin crescent, a planet must be more or less between the Earth and the Sun; only Mercury and Venus can be so placed.) First on the list is *Mars*, which may approach us to within a distance of 35 million miles. It never comes as close as Venus, and moreover it is much the smaller of the two, since its diameter is a mere 4,200 miles. Neither is it so good a reflector of sunlight. To compensate for all this, Mars is observable high in the sky against a really dark background. At its brightest, it may outshine every body in the sky apart from the Sun, the Moon and Venus.

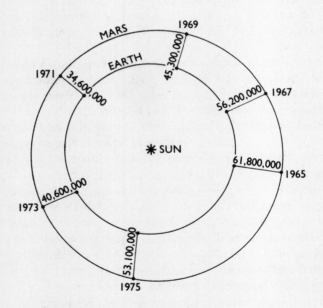

Fig. 73. Oppositions of Mars, 1965–75. The figures give the opposition distance between Mars and the Earth.

Mars is not well seen every year. As the diagram (Fig. 73) shows, it is best placed when directly opposite to the Sun in the sky—that is to say at opposition, when it will be due south at midnight. An opposition occurred on March 9, 1965. A year later, on March 9, 1966, the Earth is back at its starting-point, but Mars has not completed one circuit of the Sun; it has further to go and is travelling more slowly, so that it takes 687 Earth-days to move right round. Before another opposition can take place, the Earth will have to catch Mars up, which it will not do until April 15, 1967. Therefore, there is no opposition of Mars during 1966.

To complicate matters, the orbit of Mars is much less circular than ours, and when opposition takes place with Mars near aphelion, as in 1965, the distance between the two worlds never becomes as little as 60 million miles. The best way to bring out the differences between various op-positions is to give a table, covering the period from 1965 to 1970.

Opposition date	Minimum distance from Earth, miles	Opposition Magnitude	Position of Mars at opposition
1965 March 9	61,800,000	− 1·1	Leo, near Beta
1967 April 15	56,200,000	− 1·4	Virgo, near Spica
1969 May 31	45,300,000	− 2·1	Scorpio, near Antares
1971 August 10	34,600,000	− 2·7	Capricornus
1973 October 21	40,600,000	− 2·1	Between Pisces and Aries
1975 December 13	53,100,000	− 1·4	Taurus, near Beta

The date of opposition is not always the exact time of nearest approach. In 1967, for instance, opposition takes place on April 15, but Mars will not be at its closest to the Earth until April 21. These minor differences are unimportant, however, since Mars appears of much the same brilliancy for two or three weeks to either side of opposition.

Another fact emerges from the table. In the infuriating way so often found, Mars is always well south in the sky during favourable oppositions; in 1971, when it will pass as close to us as it ever can, it will lie in the barren group of Capricornus, and will be too low to be really well observed from Europe or the northern United States. But though this lowness of altitude is a grave handicap to telescopic workers, it does not much matter to the naked-eye viewer, and Mars will certainly be a splendid object.

The trouble about identifying Mars is that it is not always brilliant. When it exceeds zero magnitude it cannot be mistaken; its strong red colour makes it stand out at once, but when it is a long way from Earth it may sink almost to the second magnitude, looking confusingly like an ordinary star. The only safe method is to check its position in a yearly almanac. There have been many cases of unwary observers who have been deceived by it, and have jumped to the conclusion that a nova has made a sudden and dramatic appearance in the sky.

It is always interesting to check the changing position of Mars against the background, identifying a few nearby stars and making charts every few nights. It will not take long for the planet's shift to become noticeable. Careful observers will find that although the general trend is from west to east, there are times when Mars appears to stand still for a while, and then to move in the reverse direction before coming to another standstill prior to re-commencing its eastward motion. The ancient astronomers knew all about this odd behaviour, and they found it hard to explain, though they did at least realize that the old theory of a Mars moving round the Earth at a constant speed, in a perfect circle, simply would not fit the facts.

Fig. 74 shows what really happens. The Earth's velocity round the Sun is greater than that of Mars; its mean orbital speed is $18\frac{1}{2}$ miles per second, as against 15. In the diagram, the Earth is at E1 while Mars is at M1, and so on. Obviously there will be a period, while the Earth is "passing" Mars, when the apparent motion of the planet is reversed, and Mars seems to describe a loop in the sky.

The red hue of Mars is very conspicuous, and we can hardly be surprised that the planet was named in honour of the God of War. The colour is probably more marked than that of any naked-eye star; there will be a good opportunity to check this in 1969, when Mars will be at opposition near Antares in Scorpio. Mars will be three magnitudes the brighter, but

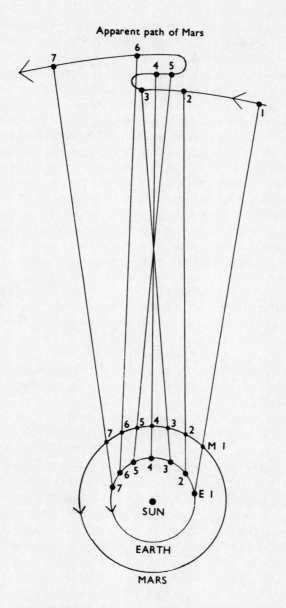

Fig. 74. Retrograde or "backward" motion of Mars among the stars.

comparisons should not be difficult.

Mars is genuinely a red world. Most of the surface is covered with what are termed "deserts", which seem to be coated with some coloured mineral; nobody is quite sure what this mineral may be, though felsite and limonite have been suggested. Telescopes show white caps at the poles, made up of some icy or frosty deposit, and there are wide dark areas which are believed to be due to living organisms, though even the close-up photographs taken with the U.S. rocket Mariner IV in July 1965 have not provided definite proof. The Martian atmosphere is thin and oxygen-poor, and while there may be a good deal of lowly "vegetation", conditions are not suitable for animal life. The brilliant Martian civilizations beloved of the story-tellers belong only to the pages of a novel, attractive though they certainly are. Water is in short supply, and there are no major lakes or seas. There are two satellites, Phobos and Deimos, both of which are dwarfs less than a dozen miles across.

So far as we are concerned, Mars is the most interesting planet in the Solar System simply because it is not sterile and lifeless. Unfortunately, large telescopes are needed to show it well. Small instruments are of little use, and binoculars will reveal nothing but a tiny reddish disk, while all that the naked-eye observer can do is to identify Mars, make estimates of its magnitude, and watch if shift as it moves slowly among the star-patterns.

I propose to spend little time in discussing the asteroids or *minor planets*, those midget worlds which move round the Sun between the orbits of Mars and Jupiter. Even the largest of them (Ceres) is a mere 430 miles in diameter, and most of the rest are extremely small. There are vast numbers of them; more than 3,000 have had their paths accurately worked out, and there may well be over 40,000 asteroids all told. A few swing away from the main swarm, and may pass relatively close to the Earth, but there is no serious danger of a head-on collision.

Only one asteroid—Vesta—can ever be seen without a telescope. It is 241 miles across, and moves round the Sun at a mean distance of 219 million miles. At its brightest it reaches the sixth magnitude, and very keen-sighted people may be able to identify it, though it looks so exactly like a dim star that the only safe method is to track its motion from one night to another. I doubt whether the average observer will be able to do this. In the late summer of 1964, for instance, Vesta lay in Aquarius, and although I could find it easily with binoculars I could never satisfy myself that I could see it without optical aid. All the other asteroids are well below naked-eye range.

Though the asteroids are the junior members of the Solar System, they are by no means devoid of interest. Their origin is uncertain. It is sometimes held that they represent the débris of an old planet (or planets) which suffered a major disaster in the remote past; alternatively, it is quite possible that they are made up of material which never formed part of a larger body, and was merely "left over", so to speak, when the main planets were born.

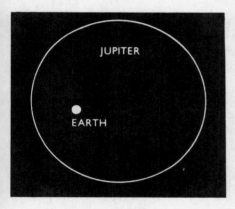

Fig. 75. Jupiter and Earth compared.

Well beyond the asteroid swarm moves *Jupiter*, giant of the Sun's family. Here we have a huge globe more than 88,000 miles in diameter as measured through its equator, and big enough to swallow over 1,300 bodies the size of the Earth. Yet there is no similarity between our world and Jupiter; the giant planet is made up of gas, principally hydrogen, and it is intensely cold, since the temperature there can never rise much above —200 degrees Fahrenheit. Obviously, life as we know it is quite out of the question.

Unlike Mars, Jupiter comes to opposition every year, simply because it moves much more slowly and the Earth takes much less time to "catch it up". The dates of the next few oppositions are:

1965 December 18. Jupiter will then be in Aries.
1967 January 20.　　,,　　,,　,,　　,,　Gemini.

1968 February 20. Jupiter will then be in Cancer.

1969 March 21.   „   „   „   „   Virgo.

1970 April 21.   „   „   „   „   Virgo.

There should be no trouble about recognition, because Jupiter is always brilliant; it never becomes faint in the same way as Mars, and it is virtually colourless as seen with the naked eye, though in a telescope its disk is decidedly yellow. The opposition magnitude ranges between -2 and $-2\frac{1}{2}$. The only possible confusion is with Venus, but even here there is little danger, and the brief notes given here should enable the rawest of beginners to distinguish between them.

Jupiter's track among the stars may be followed from night to night, though the movement is slow. Otherwise, chief interest insofar as the naked-eye observer is concerned centres upon the four large satellites, which were discovered by Galileo in the winter of 1609–10 and are extremely easy to see with any good binoculars.

The satellites are named Io, Europa, Ganymede and Callisto. The first two are comparable in size with our Moon, while the outer satellites measure 3,000 miles in diameter—larger than the planet Mercury, though admittedly not so massive. Ganymede is the brightest of them, and would be perfectly obvious with the naked eye if it lay further away from the glare of Jupiter itself. The mean magnitudes are 5·5 for Io, 5·7 for Europa, 5·0 for Ganymede and 6·3 for Callisto, so that Callisto is much the least reflective of the four. Their revolution periods round Jupiter range from 1 day $18\frac{1}{2}$ hours for Io up to 16 days $16\frac{1}{2}$ hours for Callisto.

There have been many reports from people who have been able to see two or three of the satellites with the naked eye. Exceptional sight is needed, and Jupiter must be high up against a perfectly transparent sky, but the accounts are so numerous and so well-authenticated that they must presumably be accepted. The best chance is to choose a moment when two of the satellites lie close together, so that they may show up as one object. So far as northerners are concerned, 1966 and 1967 will be good years in which to try, since Jupiter will then be well in the northern hemisphere of the sky and will be high up near the time of opposition.

Perhaps I ought to add a word of warning. It is very easy to "see" what one expects to see, so that it is wise to avoid looking up the positions of the satellites before trying to see them with the naked eye!

Saturn, the outermost of the planets known in ancient times, is a world of the same sort as Jupiter. It is somewhat smaller, with an equatorial diameter of 75,100 miles, and is much further away; its mean distance from the Sun is 886 million miles, as against 483 million for Jupiter. It too is composed of gas, and its overall density is actually less than that of water. It takes 29½ years to go once round the Sun—more than twice as long as Jupiter—and its apparent movement among the stars is very slow.

At its brightest Saturn may exceed zero magnitude, and it never becomes faint, but we have to admit that it looks very like a star, so that the only safe method of identifying it is to memorize its position. The sluggish motion means that it remains in the same part of the sky for years on end; for the whole period between 1965 and 1970, for example, it will be in the general region below the Square of Pegasus, and since there are no brilliant stars anywhere near it there should be little difficulty in finding it. Opposition details are as follows:

Opposition date	Opposition magnitude	Constellation
1965 September 6	0·8	Aquarius
1966 September 19	0·8	Pisces
1967 October 2	0·6	Pisces
1968 October 15	0·6	Pisces
1969 October 28	0·1	Between Pisces and Aries
1970 November 11	−0·1	Aries

The chart in Fig. 77 shows the approximate position of Saturn at each of these oppositions. The colour is decidedly yellow, and the planet shines with a dull light which our ancestors regarded as baleful.

Oddly enough, this uninteresting-looking planet proves to be the gem of the sky when seen through an adequate telescope, since it is surrounded by a system of rings. So far as we know, Saturn is unique in the Solar System or anywhere else. The rings are made up of vast numbers of solid particles whirling round Saturn in the manner of dwarf moons, and they are more reflective than the globe itself.

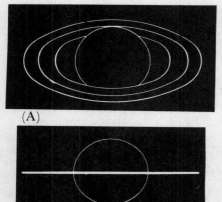

(A)

(B)

Fig. 76. In the "open" position, a considerable amount of ring-surface is presented to us (A). Saturn is then a magnitude brighter than when the rings are edge-on (B).

Though the ring-system measures 170,000 miles from one side to the other, it is not more than ten miles thick, so that when the rings are edge-on to us they practically disappear. This is a matter for the telescopic observer, since the rings cannot possibly be seen with the naked eye, and even binoculars can do no more than show that there is something unusual about Saturn's shape.[1] However, the angle of the ring-system has a marked effect upon the naked-eye magnitude. Saturn looks much brighter when the rings are open than when they are edgeways-on (Fig. 76). In 1966, Saturn will never be much more brilliant than Aldebaran; by 1970, it will surpass Capella.

Until 1781 it was thought that the Solar System must be complete—partly because seven was the magical number, and there were seven bright bodies all told: the Sun, the Moon and the five known planets. It was therefore a major surprise when William Herschel, then an obscure amateur, discovered an object which proved to be a new planet, now called *Uranus*.

Herschel did not at once realize what he had found. He mistook it for a comet, and not until the orbit was worked out did astronomers learn that it was something much more significant. Uranus is a giant; it has a diameter of less than

[1] We must reject the various claims that Saturn may be seen elongated with the naked eye. Neither is there the slightest chance of seeing even the largest of its nine satellites, Titan.

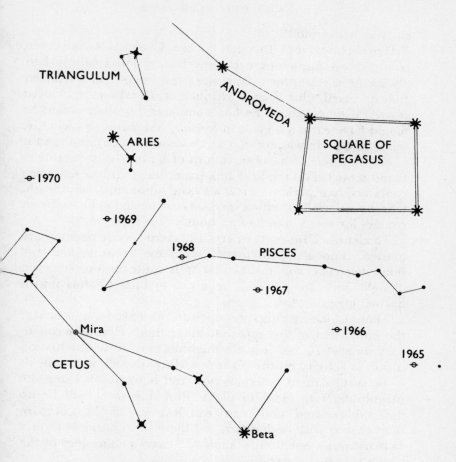

Fig. 77. Opposition Positions of Saturn, 1965–70.

30,000 miles, so that it is by no means the equal of Jupiter or Saturn, but it could still hold fifty globes the size of the Earth. It is gaseous, and its surface temperature is remarkably low.

Though Uranus is so remote (1,783 million miles from the Sun at its mean distance), it is distinctly visible to the naked eye when best placed. The mean opposition magnitude is 5·7, and keen-sighted people will be able to make it out once they know where it is. From 1965 to 1968 it will be in Leo, after which it will pass into Virgo and stay there until 1975; it is not a rapid mover. Yearly almanacs give its position against the star background.

Herschel was not the first to see Uranus. It had been recorded on numerous occasions before 1781, but it had always been taken for a faint star, and nobody had realized that it moved. One French astronomer, Le Monnier, charted it several times, and if he had compared his observations he would have earned a place in history, but this is just what he failed to do. He was not of a methodical turn of mind, and it is said that one of his observations of Uranus was eventually found scrawled on the back of a paper bag that had had once contained hair perfume. (It is also said, apparently with truth, that he quarrelled with everybody with whom he came in contact for more than half an hour.)

To identify Uranus, keen eyes and considerable patience are needed. Binoculars, of course, will show it easily, and any small telescope will reveal that it is quite unstarlike, even though moderate power is required to turn Uranus into a distinct greenish disk.

There is one investigation open to the naked-eye watcher: the estimation of the apparent magnitude. Uranus seems to vary somewhat, and it is possible that part of the fluctuation is due to activity on the planet's surface, though it is difficult to be sure. Patient observers will find it worth checking the magnitude from night to night. Probably there will be no detectable change, and in any case it is very hard to compare faint objects with each other, but there is no harm in trying. It is naturally essential to know the exact magnitudes of the stars used for comparison.

Uranus marks the limit of the planetary system so far as the unequipped observer is concerned. We need do no more than pause to mention the outermost members of the Sun's family, the giant *Neptune* and the small, puzzling *Pluto*, since both are hopelessly invisible without optical aid. Neptune never becomes as bright as the seventh magnitude, and Pluto is beyond the range of binoculars or small telescopes.

There are rare occasions when two or more planets lie close together in the sky. These conjunctions are not in the least important, but they are interesting to observe, mainly because they are so unusual. Even occultations of one planet by another are not unknown. On October 3, 1590 Venus

passed in front of Mars, and hid it briefly; the whole phenomenon is said to have been watched by Michael Möstlin,
professor of mathematics at the University of Heidelberg, and
this observation must have been made with the naked eye,
since the telescope did not come on the scene until early in the
following century. On July 21, 1859 Venus and Jupiter passed
so near each other that they could not be separated without
optical aid, and there are various other records of close
approaches. Of course, such conjunctions are due to nothing
more fundamental than line of sight effects, as the planets
concerned are nowhere near each other in space.[1]

Planetary groupings are also uncommon, but on June 22,
1881 Venus, Mars, Jupiter, Saturn and the crescent Moon all
lay in Aries, while much more recently—in February 1962—
there was a gathering of planets in Capricornus, consisting of
Mercury, Venus, Mars, Jupiter and Saturn. This last grouping
was not visible with the naked eye, or indeed with a telescope,
since the Sun was not far off and all the planets passed below
the horizon very soon after sunset, but astrologers and other
cranks made the most of it. In India, where astrology still
retains a strangle-hold upon many people, there were wide-
widespread panics, and the end of the world was confidently
expected—all of which goes to show that we of the "en-
lightened" twentieth century cannot afford to laugh too loudly
at our forbears who believed the Earth to be flat.

Planets can also occult stars, but it will be a very long time
before a first-magnitude star is involved. The last occasion was
on July 7, 1959, when Venus occulted Regulus. Unfortunately
the event took place in the early afternoon, with the Sun high
in the sky; I was able to observe it with a powerful telescope,
but it was quite undetectable with the naked eye.

It is true that no useful observations of the planets can be
made without optical aid, but this is no reason for ignoring
them. The observer who tracks down Mercury in the evening
twilight, tries to see the crescent of Venus, checks the magnitude and motion of Mars, identifies Jupiter and Saturn, and

[1] A particularly close modern conjunction was that of May 1955, when Jupiter
and Uranus were close together. I had excellent telescopic views of it, but of course
Uranus could not be seen with the naked eye. For some nights it looked rather like
an extra satellite of Jupiter, though larger and dimmer than the four real satellites.

does his best to make out the dim speck of Uranus may be contributing nothing to scientific knowledge, but he is at least teaching himself—and enjoying himself at the same time.

Chapter Nineteen

SUN AND MOON

MOST BOOKS ABOUT popular astronomy devote a great deal
of space to the Sun and Moon. This is perfectly proper, since
both show features which are easy to study with a small
telescope; the Sun has its spots, while the surface of the Moon
is covered with mountains, craters, plains and valleys. Much
of our knowledge of the lunar surface is due to the work of
amateur astronomers equipped with modest instruments, and
there is still wide scope, even though professional observers
have now entered the field.

With the naked eye alone, matters are very different. Nothing useful can be accomplished, and there is very little to be
said—so I propose to be brief.

Just as the Sun dominates the daytime sky, so the Moon is
pre-eminent at night. When the Moon is full, it is brilliant
indeed, and there have been people who have estimated its
brightness as a quarter or even half of that of the Sun. Nothing
could be further from the truth. The Moon can never send us
more than 1/450,000 of the Sun's light, and even if the sky
were completely covered with full moons we should still receive
only one-fifth of the Sun's brilliance. In more scientific terms,
the intensity of moonlight is one-quarter of a metre-candle, a
metre-candle being the light produced by a candle which is one
metre (39·4 inches) away. If you darken a room, light a candle
and then stand just over three feet away from it, you will
receive as much luminosity as can ever be shed by the Moon.
A forty-watt bulb at fifteen yards will produce the same
intensity.

The Moon has a diameter of only 2,160 miles, so that it is
small compared with the planets. On the other hand it is
extremely close to us on the astronomical scale; its orbit is not
perfectly circular, and its distance is therefore variable, but it
is always more than 221,000 miles and less than 253,000 miles,
giving a mean of just under 239,000 miles. To make a scale
model of the Earth-Moon system, all that need be done is to

take a tennis-ball, wrap a cord round it ten times, and then unravel the cord, placing a table-tennis ball at the far end. The model is not precise, but it is a good approximation.

Under the circumstances, the Moon might be expected to look more brilliant than it actually does. The explanation is that the lunar surface is a very poor reflector; that is to say, it has a low albedo. It reflects only about 7% of the sunlight which falls upon it, as against over 60% for the cloud-covered planet Venus. And far from being bluish-white, moonlight is decidedly yellow. In passing, no colours can be seen by moonlight, because the intensity is too low. If you are walking along a dark road illuminated only by the Moon, and you happen to come across a coloured poster, it will be quite impossible to tell what hue the poster really is.

The Moon shines because it reflects the light of the Sun, but it is also illuminated by the Earth. From the Moon, earthlight would be brilliant, partly because the Earth is a larger body and partly because it is a better reflector—its albedo has been estimated at 40% or so. When the Moon appears as a crescent, the light reflected from Earth lights up the "dark" side, producing the effect which country-folk used to call "The Old Moon in the Young Moon's arms". The intensity of the earthshine depends upon conditions in our own air, but it is often very striking indeed. Its cause has been known for several hundreds of years, and Leonardo da Vinci, the fifteenth-century "universal genius" who painted superb pictures, undertook scientific experiments and even gave some thought to a flying machine, explained it quite correctly. The earthlit Moon is a familiar sight, and a beautiful one.

Our remote cave-dwelling ancestors must have been well acquainted with the Moon's phases, or apparent changes of shape from new to full. The phases were in no way puzzling to the Greek philosophers of long ago, even though some curious legends have been associated with them in more modern times.[1] The diagram given on page 183 has been used many times before, but it is simple and clear, so that there is no reason to modify it. The Moon is new at position 1, half

[1] I particularly like the tale told by the African Bushmen, who believe that the Moon once offended the Sun, and is regularly pierced by the solar rays until he pleads for mercy and is gradually restored.

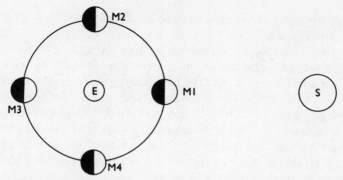

Fig. 78. Phases of the Moon. S—Sun; E—Earth; M1 to
M4—the Moon in four different positions in its orbit.
Not to scale.

(First Quarter) at 2, full at 3, and half again (Last Quarter) at
4. The proper New Moon is invisible, because the Moon is
then practically between the Earth and the Sun, so that its
dark side is turned in our direction; it is wrong to call the thin
evening crescent "new moon", as most people do.

Check the position of the Moon from night to night, and
you will see that it is moving eastward against the starry
background. It covers about 13 degrees in 24 hours, so that in
one hour it shifts about half a degree or the same distance as its
own apparent diameter. Clearly, it will rise later every night.
The "retardation", or delay in moonrise from one night to the
next, is generally more than three-quarters of an hour, but
the situation in September is somewhat different, because during
autumn the Moon's path in the sky makes a comparatively
sharp angle with the horizon. This is the time of Harvest Moon.

Consider Fig. 79, which shows the position of the ecliptic
in spring and in autumn. (The Moon's path does not lie
exactly along the ecliptic, but it is not far off, and in a diagram of this sort the error does not matter.) In spring, the
Moon moves from A to B in 24 hours, so that it must rise
much later by the time it has reached B. In autumn, the Moon
moves from A′ to B′ in 24 hours, but the difference in rising-
time will not be so great, and may be reduced to only 20
minutes or so. The September full moon will shine brightly
in the evening sky for several nights in succession, though it
is not true to say, as most books do, that the Moon rises at

almost the same time for a week or so. The following full moon is termed Hunter's Moon.

It has often been stated that the Harvest Moon looks particularly big, and people have described it to me as appearing "the size of a dinner-plate". Actually, Harvest Moon looks no larger than any other full moon, and in any case the Moon is a surprisingly small object in our skies. A disk one-fifth of an inch in diameter held at arm's length will cover it. Anybody who doubts this has only to cut out a disk of the same size as that given in Fig. 80, and then try the experiment for himself.

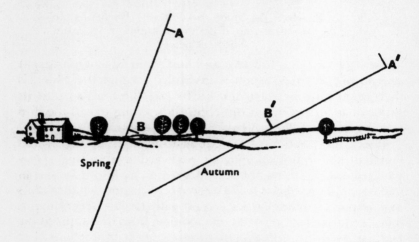

Fig. 79. Harvest Moon.

Moreover, to describe the Moon as being the size of a dinner-plate is about as useful as saying that it looks as big as a piece of china. To measure the apparent diameter of a celestial object in yards, feet or inches is impossible, and the only method is to use angular measure; the Moon submits an angle of roughly half a degree, which is not very much. Artists who paint beautiful moonlit scenes never fail to exaggerate the apparent size of the Moon, though this is excusable on the grounds of artistic licence.[1]

[1] I am referring, of course, to real artists—not modern "painters", who would be more likely to depict the Moon as a gamboge corkscrew or as a shapeless blob with holes running through it.

Another popular misconception is that the full moon looks largest when it is low down, and shrinks in apparent size as it rises above the horizon. This celebrated "Moon Illusion" has been known for two thousand years at least, and has led to innumerable arguments.

Nobody doubts the illusion; to the casual observer, a low-down full moon seems enormous. Measure it, using your 1/5-inch disk (or, for that matter, a half-penny held at nine feet from the eye) and you will see that it *is* an illusion and nothing more. When low, the full moon is no larger than when riding high in the sky. The obvious explanation is that the observer is unconsciously comparing the Moon with objects along the horizon, such as trees and houses, but it seems that we cannot dispose of the effect so easily. The illusion is still marked when the Moon is rising over a sea horizon, where there are no adjacent objects to act as comparisons.

Fig. 80. Held at arm's length, this disk will cover the full Moon!

It has also been suggested that the illusion is due to the mechanism of the human eye, so that an object appears larger when viewed horizontally. Lying on one's back and observing from a prone position shows that this idea will not do either, and nowadays most people have come back to a theory put forward by no less a person than Ptolemy, the second-century star-catalogue compiler. According to Ptolemy's "apparent-distance" explanation, any object seen across filled space, such as the Moon when near the horizon, will seem to be further away than an object which is seen across empty space, such as the Moon when high up. If the images of the two objects are really equal in size, then the one which seems further away will give the impression of being the larger.

At all events, the illusion has nothing to do with the Moon itself, and so it is not strictly astronomical. It is usually said that people with only one eye, or who deliberately cover up one eye for several hours before observing, are not subject to the illusion. I am dubious about this, because a friend of mine who was blinded in one eye during the war has told me that he never fails to notice the illusion, while when I tried the eye-covering experiment I found that it made no difference at all.

On the whole, Ptolemy's theory seems to be the best answer.

Occasionally the Moon is seen to be encircled by a ring of light. This is a lunar halo, due to a thin layer of ice-crystal cloud high in the Earth's atmosphere. Since it too is basically non-astronomical, notes about it are best deferred until Chapter 22. Instead, let us turn to the markings on the lunar surface.

The Moon is a world without atmosphere, without water, and—so far as we can tell—without life. Its surface is marked by the dark areas known as seas, once thought to be oceans but now known to be wide dry plains without a trace of moisture in them. There are high mountains, almost innumerable hills and valleys, and tens of thousands of the walled circular formations which are always called "craters". The largest crater on the Moon measures almost 190 miles from side to side, while the photographs taken from the American rockets Ranger VIII and IX in 1965 show tiny pits less than one foot in diameter and a few inches deep. There is little truly level ground on the Moon.

Nobody is quite sure how the craters were formed; my own view is that the large formations are volcanic, but arguments are still going on. Incidentally, the Moon keeps the same face toward us all the time, so that the various features keep to the same positions on the disk. The reverse side of the Moon can never be seen from Earth, though it was successfully photographed in 1959, when the Russians sent a rocket on a round trip and were able to obtain pictures.

Look at the Moon, and you will be able to make out many of the dark patches. Some time ago, during the preparation of this book, I enlisted the aid of various observers, some experienced and some beginners, and asked them to draw the lunar disk without optical aid—see Plate VIII.

The most interesting part of the experiment was the attempt to see whether naked-eye observations could be used to draw up a lunar map of even approximate accuracy. It seems that the system of dark plains can be plotted quite well; for instance, the Mare Crisium is easily seen as a detached "mare", while the well-formed Mare Serenitatis and Mare Imbrium are distinctly separable. The forked appearance of the Mare Nectaris-Mare Fœcunditatis region is also an obvious feature, and most people could see the lighter grey strip of the irregular

Mare Frigoris. Using all the charts I collected, it would be quite possible to produce a reasonable map. Yet apparently nobody did so before telescopes entered the scene in the early 17th century, and even the early telescopic charts are strangely inaccurate.

What cannot be done, of course, is to chart the craters. Only a few may be recognized at all; Clavius, because of its size (almost 150 miles in diameter) is visible only when on the terminator, and though Copernicus and a few others may be identified because of their brilliance they do not look like craters unless some sort of optical aid is used. Moreover, the southern part of the Moon appears virtually blank, even though it is in fact exceptionally rough and is covered with craters of all shapes and sizes. Consequently, naked-eye observers of past ages could not have had any hopes of finding out what the Moon's surface is really like. Even so, one is left with the impression that they could have done much better than they actually did.

Comparison of the drawings with a photograph of the full moon shows that the agreement is quite good, bearing in mind that some people draw better than others. The separate map shows all the features which may possibly be seen with the naked eye.

The Moon's surface is very uneven; there are mountain chains towering to well over 20,000 feet, and it may even be that some of the peaks are loftier than our Everest, though comparisons are difficult in view of the fact that the Moon has no water-level to act as a standard of reference. The Apennines, forming part of the border of the Mare Imbrium, are the most spectacular of the mountains, and indications of them will be seen when they are best placed. This means that they must be caught when near the terminator, or boundary between the daylit and night hemispheres, with the Moon slightly more than half-phase. The immense crater Clavius, nearly 150 miles across, may also be seen occasionally, appearing as a dent in the terminator.

Binoculars, of course, will show the seas clearly, together with many craters, while a small telescope will bring out so many details that to map them at one sitting would be a hopeless task.

There is no need to do more than mention the Man in the Moon, who has been the subject of so many legends—according to a German tale, he was a villager who was caught in the act of stealing his neighbour's cabbages, and was placed in the Moon to act as an awful warning to other would-be thieves! The arrangement of the dark plains can, I suppose, be said to give a vague impression of a human face, though I am bound to admit that I have never been able to recognize the Old Man properly. With any optical aid he disappears, lost in a mass of detail.

During the crescent stage, when the Moon first emerges from the twilight, the well-marked plain known as the Mare Crisium (Sea of Crises) should be looked for; as the phase increases, other plains come into view, while after full moon the Mare Crisium is one of the first features to disappear. It is interesting to make regular drawings, and see which features can be made out. Incidentally, it is worth noting that half-moon is only one-ninth as bright as full moon, partly because the intensity of light falls off near the terminator and partly because the craters and mountains cast long shadows. The "evening" half-moon, or First Quarter, is moreover rather brighter than the "morning" half-moon or Last Quarter, because the eastern[1] side of the Moon, visible after full, contains more dark plains.

Though the Moon appears brilliant, and will dazzle anyone who looks straight at it, it is quite harmless. Not so with the Sun, which is not also brilliant but is also intensely hot. Its surface temperature is 6,000 degrees Centigrade, and anyone who looks straight at it through a telescope, or even a pair of binoculars, is certain to be permanently blinded; there have been many accidents in the past, and even dark filters are unsafe, since they cannot afford complete protection and are always liable to splinter without warning. The only sensible way to observe the Sun through a telescope or binoculars is to project the solar image on to a white screen, keeping one's eye well away from the eyepiece. I have published many drawings of the sort shown in Fig. 81, as well as showing them on tele-

[1] By convention, the Mare Crisium is said to be in the western hemisphere of the Moon, while the Mare Imbrium extends over to the east. Recently, the U.S. Air Force moon-mappers have decided to alter this, making east west and west east, so producing immense confusion for no good reason whatsoever.

vision, but I make no apology for repeating myself, because the danger is so real.

Neither is it wise to look straight at the Sun with the naked eye. If a dark filter is used—a well-smoked piece of glass, for instance—there is no serious risk, but the filter must be very dark indeed, and it is best to wait until the Sun is very low or shrouded in mist.

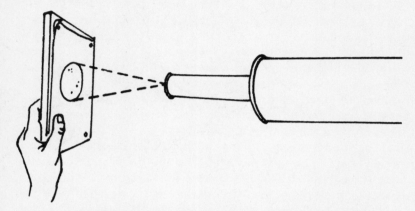

Fig. 81. The simple method of projecting the solar image.

The most obvious features on the Sun's surface are the spots, dark patches which may attain immense size. The Sun itself has a diameter of 864,000 miles, and is big enough to hold more than a million globes the size of the Earth, so that everything there is on a vast scale; even a comparatively small sunspot is much larger than our world. The spots look dark, but in fact they appear so only because they are cooler than the surrounding surface. Their temperature is a mere 4,000 degrees Centigrade.

The Sun is gaseous, and can obviously retain no permanent markings. The life of any particular sunspot may amount to no more than a few hours, while the record for longevity seems to be held by a spot seen in 1943, which lasted for nine months. The spot was not in constant view. The Sun rotates on its axis in a period of about 25 days, so that a spot is carried slowly across the disk, taking roughly a fortnight to pass from one side to the other. In a further fortnight it will reappear at the opposite edge of the Sun's face, provided that it still exists.

The Sun has a well-marked cycle of activity. Every eleven years, at solar maximum, spots and spot-groups are frequent; activity then dies down, until at solar minimum, as in 1964, the disk may be clear of spots for many days at a time. After

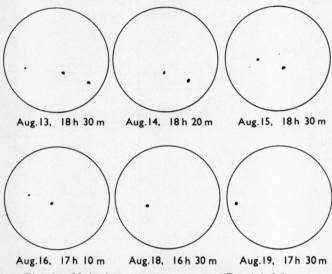

Fig. 82. Naked-eye sunspots, 1947. Patrick Moore.

minimum, things start to become more interesting again until another maximum is reached.

The cause of the solar cycle is not known, and for that matter we are still rather in the dark as to the origin of the sunspots themselves. Many theories have been put forward, but uncertainties remain, even though great advances in our knowledge have been made during the last few decades.

Around the time of maximum there may be various spots which become large enough to be seen with the naked eye, either when the Sun is seen through mist or else when a dark filter is used. I well remember the spot-group of April 1947, which at its greatest development covered an area of over seven million square miles; it was an easy naked-eye object, and so were other groups seen around the energetic solar maximum of 1957–58. No such spots are to be expected during 1965 or 1966, but there should be several of them by the time of the next maximum. So far as can be estimated, this should be in 1969–70, but it is impossible to be sure, because the solar cycle is not perfectly regular.

When a naked-eye spot is seen it is likely to remain on view for several days, and will persist either until it shrinks or until it is carried toward the Sun's edge. There is a certain value in noting the numbers of naked-eye spots seen during each year, but it is not a study which I personally recommend, because I know how easy it is to damage one's eyesight. The best course is to wait until near solar maximum and then look when the Sun is low down, preferably misty as well. Always use a dark glass.

As the Sun drops toward the horizon it seems to become distorted, and looks flattened. This is due to the effects of the Earth's atmosphere, which bends or refracts the sunlight. The closer the object is to the horizon, the greater the amount of refraction; the Sun's lower limb is therefore more subject to it, and the apparent flattening is the result. Refraction tends to lift up any object which is at the horizon, and it is possible to see the Sun even after it has theoretically set. There are a few cases on record of the Sun and the full moon having been observed simultaneously at opposite horizons; both were actually below the horizon-line, but both were visible, because refraction had lifted their images into view.

Occasionally the last segment of the Sun's disk flashes brilliant green before it disappears from sight. The Green Flash is said to be very impressive, and has been photographed on various occasions. It, too, is due to refraction in the Earth's atmosphere; the greenness is caused because the blue light from the Sun is removed by scattering in the air, while the red light is removed by atmospheric water-vapour. Sunlight is a mixture of all the colours of the rainbow, and the sky appears blue because the blue component is most easily scattered.

I admit that I have yet to see the Green Flash, though I have often looked for it. The best hope is to watch the Sun setting over a sea horizon, but conditions must be ideal, and an observer who makes up his mind to catch the vivid green ray will have to resign himself to watching many sunsets without result.

Chapter Twenty

CELESTIAL HIDE-AND-SEEK

OF ALL THE sights provided by nature, that of a total eclipse of the Sun is probably the most breath-taking. I have been fortunate enough to see two total eclipses, and I imagine nothing more awe-inspiring. It is not surprising that eclipse records go back for thousands of years.

The Earth revolves round the Sun; the Moon revolves round the Earth. Therefore, there must be times when the new moon passes exactly between the Earth and the Sun. By sheer

Fig. 83. Theory of a solar eclipse. S—Sun; M—Moon; E—Earth. The diagram is not to scale.

coincidence—so far as we can tell, it is nothing more—the Moon and Sun appear almost the same size in the sky, with angular diameters of half a degree each, so that the Moon is just able to cover up the Sun. This is the cause of a solar eclipse.

Fig. 83 should make the situation clear. The cone of shadow cast by the Moon is only just long enough to reach the Earth's surface, while to either side of the totality zone the Sun will be partly hidden. The belt of totality can never be more than 170 miles wide, and no total eclipse can last for as long as nine minutes. Generally, the Sun is fully hidden for only a minute or two.

On an average there are two or three solar eclipses each year, but only a few of them are total, and it usually happens that the zone of totality lies in some inaccessible region; thus the eclipse of November 2, 1967, will be total only in An- tarctica, while that of September 22, 1968 will be total only in parts of North Russia. This explains why relatively few people have ever seen one. The last to be visible in England took place in 1927; the next will not occur until 1999, and even then it will be seen only from parts of Cornwall, while over the rest of Britain it will be partial. Moreover, most solar eclipses are not total over any part of the Earth's surface, since it is rare for the lining-up of the three bodies to be sufficiently exact.

It is natural to ask why we do not see an eclipse at every new moon. The answer is that the Moon's orbit is tilted at an angle of just over 5 degrees with respect to that of the Earth, so that at most new moons there is no lining-up and therefore no eclipse; the Moon passes unseen either above or below the Sun in the sky. Obviously, a solar eclipse can happen only at new moon.[1]

A total eclipse is important because as soon as the last portion of the Sun's disk is hidden, the dark body of the Moon is seen to be surrounded by a glorious pearly light known as the corona. The corona has nothing to do with the Moon; it may be termed the outer atmosphere of the Sun, and is made up of very thin gas (mainly hydrogen) at a strangely high temperature. Because it is relatively faint, it is quite invisible to the naked eye except at a total eclipse, and neither will any ordinary telescope show it.

The corona stretches outward from the Sun for millions of miles, though since it has no sharp boundary we cannot give an exact figure for its "depth". At times of sunspot maximum there are long coronal streamers stretching across the sky, but when the Sun is near its minimum the outline of the corona is much more regular. The form of the corona depends, in fact, on the state of the solar cycle.

Below the corona lies the chromosphere, marking the lower atmosphere of the Sun. It is in the chromosphere that we find the brilliant red patches which used to be called Red Flames, but which are now known as prominences. They certainly look red, but they are not flames; they are made up of incandescent gas, principally hydrogen, and they are of vast

[1] Rider Haggard, the great story-teller, once made a curious blunder here. In the original edition of his classic novel *King Solomon's Mines*, he described a full moon, a total solar eclipse, and another full moon on successive nights. In later editions, when the mistake had been pointed out, he replaced his eclipse of the Sun by an eclipse of the Moon.

size, since the length of an average prominence is around 125,000 miles.

Complex modern instruments make it possible to study the prominences at any time, without waiting for an eclipse, but it is only during totality that they are visible with the naked eye. Sometimes they are very striking, particularly when the Sun is near the peak of its cycle. Unfortunately it is essential for the Sun's disk to be completely hidden; 99% will not do, since it is only after the last sliver of the bright solar face has been hidden by the advancing Moon that the prominences, the chromosphere and the corona leap into view.

Professional astronomers are always ready to make long journeys to study total eclipses, because there are certain investigations which cannot be carried out at any other time. This means that there is no opportunity for casual gazing, and one professional told me some years ago that although he had observed half a dozen total eclipses he had never really "seen" one—he had been too busy checking, photographing and carrying out various specialized tasks. The amateur who merely wants to look at a total eclipse is not so limited, and for this purpose the naked eye is sufficient. Any optical aid lessens the beauty of the effect.

The chances for useful work are restricted, but some interesting studies may be carried out. It is worth while to make meteorological observations, such as the effect upon wind velocity, barometric pressure, and temperature; wet and dry bulb thermometers may be used to measure the change in humidity or wetness of the air. Also, there are the shadow bands, curious wavy lines which appear over the Earth's surface just before totality. They are due to atmospheric effects, and belong more to meteorology than to astronomy, but although they are usually faint they should always be looked for. They have never been properly photographed, so far as I know, and it would be interesting to record them. The best method would be to arrange some broad, white surface upon which the shadow-bands would be seen to advantage. I tried to do this during the 1954 eclipse in Sweden, but without success.

Shadow-bands depend upon the state of the Earth's atmosphere at the observing site, and are not always seen. If they can be glimpsed, the following data should be recorded: the time during which bands are visible, their numbers, their movements, their spacing, whether or not they are also visible during totality itself, and whether they are hazy or clear-cut. Information of this sort is definitely valuable, and professional astronomers have no time to obtain it.

In mid-totality it is often possible to see stars, together with any planets which happen to be suitably placed. Generally speaking, all first-magnitude stars and some of the second magnitude should be visible if the sky is really clear, but I cannot speak from first-hand knowledge; in 1954 there was enough cloud to hide all but the very brightest objects, and in 1961 conditions were even less favourable, so that only Venus came into view.

At one eclipse, that of 1878, a serious search was made for a planet which was thought to move round the Sun at a distance less than that of Mercury. The hypothetical planet had even been given a name—Vulcan—and the French astronomer Le Verrier, one of the leading theorists of the time, was convinced of its existence. Two Americans, Watson and Swift, sketched the stars which became visible round the eclipsed Sun, and concluded that they had found several new planets, but it now seems certain that they were wrong. Vulcan does not exist; the objects recorded by Watson and Swift were merely faint stars in the constellation of Cancer.

Yet there is no reason why some observers who are anxious to carry out an unusual programme should not do their best to plot the star-fields round the hidden Sun. The chances of finding any unknown body are vanishingly small, but they do exist. Of course, a planet such as Le Verrier's Vulcan would be unobservable except during a total eclipse, since it would be much too close to the Sun in the sky. The only other chance of detecting it would be to catch it in the act of passing in transit across the solar disk.

Glorious photographs of the corona are taken at every solar eclipse during which clouds do not interfere, and this makes ordinary sketching rather pointless, but at least a drawing made during totality is an impressive personal memento. It is more valuable to note the colour of the corona and chromosphere, and see just how far the coronal rays may be traced; for drawings of this sort, white chalk on dark blue paper is probably the best material. Unfortunately everything happens in a hurry, and there is not time to carry out careful checks. An observer who wants to undertake this programme should be careful not to dazzle himself by looking at the Sun until the eclipse has become total.

Two other eclipse phenomena may be seen with the naked eye. Just before totality the Sun's disk shines out between high peaks on the mountainous limb of the Moon, producing the effect known as Baily's Beads, while at the end of totality the first portion of the sun to reappear from behind the Moon gives the impression of a wonderful "diamond ring". It is sometimes possible, too, to see the Moon's advancing shadow, which rushes across the landscape at a terrifying speed.

Now and then there are attempts to carry out what may be termed "off-beat" programmes, and I cannot resist relating one of them, because I was concerned in it. It was carried out during the total eclipse of February 15, 1961, when the track of totality crossed France, Italy, Jugoslavia and into Russia, which is shown on Plate VII*a*. Some months earlier I had had the idea that it might be possible to show the eclipse on television, using teams stationed at various points along the track. The scheme was taken up by the BBC, and then by Eurovision, so that there was extensive coverage.[1]

The programme was very successful. I was dispatched to the top of a remote mountain in Jugoslavia, with a camera team, and though clouds proved to be a nuisance they did clear away in time for us to see the "diamond ring". Previously I had been battling with difficulties, since my links with Eurovision Control in Milan had broken down and I was completely out of touch with everyone, but I judged the timing as well as I could, and by sheer luck managed to come "on the air" at the right moment.

Meanwhile, the Jugoslav camera director was a man with ideas of his own. I was unaware of them, because I cannot talk Serbo-Croat, and to establish communication we had to use a somewhat cumbersome method. (I talked French to a

---

[1] At the preliminary Eurovision conference, held in Paris in January, the Spanish Television Service was also represented. When I pointed out that the track of totality did not cross the Iberian peninsula anywhere, the Spanish producer said, rather peevishly: "But cannot this be altered?"

Belgian astronomer, who relayed it to the director in German, after which it was passed on to the camera crew in Serbo-Croat.) The director had heard that at the moment of totality, when the sky becomes dark, animals become drowsy. He therefore tethered several mountain oxen in full view and trained cameras on them, so that during totality he could switch over and show the animals duly going to sleep. Just to make sure that everyone could see them properly, he floodlit them. . . .

Partial eclipses are tame by comparison, and the naked-eye observer can do no more than note the increasing "bite" out of the Sun as the Moon advances. There is one further type of eclipse: the annular. If exact lining-up occurs when the Moon is at its greatest distance from the Earth, the lunar disk appears smaller than that of the Sun, and cannot provide a complete screen. At mid-eclipse, therefore, the dark body of the Moon is seen surrounded by a ring of brilliant sunlight. Neither the corona nor the prominences come into view.

Eclipses of the Sun due in the near future are as follows:

1965 November 23, 4h 11m. Annular in Borneo area. Invisible in Britain.

1966 May 20, 9h 43m. Partial in Britain. Very short totality in parts of Turkey and Balkan area; annular elsewhere along the central line (North Africa to South Russia).

1966 November 12, 14.27. Total in parts of the North Pacific and South American area. Invisible in Britain.

1967 May 9, 14.57. Partial. Invisible in Britain.

1967 November 2, 5h 48m. Total in Antarctica. Invisible in Britain.

1968 March 28, 22h 48m. Partial. Invisible in Britain.

1968 September 22, 11h 9m. Total in parts of North Russia. Partial in Britain.

1969 March 18, 4h 52m. Annular in New Guinea area. Invisible in Britain.

1969 September 11, 19h 56m. Annular in North Pacific and parts of South America. Invisible in Britain.

1970 March 7, 17h 43m. Total in Mexico, Central Pacific. Invisible in Britain.

1970 August 31, 22h 2m. Annular in South Pacific. Invisible in Britain.

1971 February 25, 9h 49m. Fairly large partial in Britain. Not total anywhere.

1971 July 22, 9h 15m. Partial. Invisible in Britain.

1971 August 20, 22h 54m. Partial. Invisible in Britain.

1972 January 16, 10h 53m. Annular in Antarctica. Invisible in Britain.

1972 July 10, 19h 39m. Partial in Britain near sunset. Total in Japan and Canada area.

The next total eclipses visible anywhere in Britain will be those of August 11, 1999 (Cornwall) and September 23, 2090.

Let me repeat my earlier warning. It is most unwise to look straight at the Sun during the partial phase, even with the use of a dark filter. A quick glance can do no harm, but to stare for any appreciable period will have unpleasant after-effects. During the last really large partial eclipse visible in England, that of 1954, there were quite a number of people who damaged their eyes in this way. Much the best method is to use a telescope, projecting the Sun's image on to a screen without looking through the eyepiece direct. If no telescope is available, be very careful indeed—and on no account risk a glance through binoculars.

An eclipse of the Moon is a very different matter. Here there is no obstructing body; since the Moon is the closest natural object in the sky, nothing can block it out. What happens is that the Moon passes into the Earth's shadow, so that all direct sunlight is cut off.

The Earth casts a long shadow in space. The principal cone, termed the umbra, is about 860,000 miles long; this is more than three times the distance of the Moon from the Earth, so that at the mean distance of the Moon (239,000 miles) the cone has a diameter of 5,700 miles or so. When the Moon passes into the centre of the umbra, it may take $1\frac{3}{4}$ hours to travel right through. This, of course, is the length of totality—very different from the few fleeting moments of a total eclipse of the Sun. And since the Sun is a disk, not a point source of light, the umbra cone is surrounded to either side by the penumbra or area of partial shadow, as shown in Fig. 84.

The Moon depends upon reflected sunlight, but it does not generally disappear even at mid-totality. This is because the blanket of atmosphere surrounding the Earth acts in rather the manner of a lens, and bends some of the sunlight on to the lunar surface. In most eclipses the Moon simply turns a dim, rather coppery colour until it emerges from the shadow. Eclipses of the Moon may be either total or partial.

Telescopic observers often record lovely colours during lunar eclipses; there are reds, greens and blues. Everything

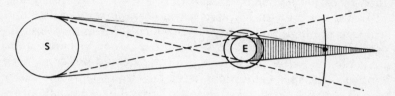

Fig. 84. Theory of a lunar eclipse. S—Sun; E—Earth;
m—the position of the Moon at mid-totality.
The diagram is not to scale.

depends upon the state of the Earth's air, since all the sunlight reaching the eclipsed Moon has to pass through our air *en route*. Unfortunately these colours are not well seen without optical aid, though at some eclipses the naked-eye Moon is decidedly pink. This was the case on January 29, 1953, when the effect was very striking indeed.

Lunar eclipses are no more common than eclipses of the Sun, but they are more often seen from any one place on the Earth's surface. This is because a solar eclipse, as we have noted on page 192, is visible only over a restricted area, whereas an eclipse of the Moon will be seen over a complete hemisphere of the Earth. Thus there will be no less than nine total lunar eclipses seen from Europe between 1967 and 1987, together with various partials.

Before the Moon enters the main cone, it is bound to pass through the penumbral zone; there are also penumbral eclipses, when the Moon misses the main shadow altogether. These are hard to detect with the naked eye, and nothing can be seen apart from a slight dimming of one part of the surface, but they are worth looking for. Most books say that they are invisible without special instruments, but I have collected enough reports to satisfy myself that the approach of the penumbral shadow is easily perceptible under good conditions of observation.

The main interest for the naked-eye watcher concerns the colour and brightness of the eclipsed Moon. Sometimes the Moon is still very prominent at mid-totality, but there are exceptions. For instance, the eclipses of December 30, 1963 and June 25, 1964 were exceptionally dark, because some months earlier a violent volcanic outburst from Mount Agung, at Bali in the East Indies, had sent a vast quantity of dust and ash into the high atmosphere of the Earth. From my observatory at East Grinstead, in Sussex, the Moon became quite invisible soon after totality on June 25; I could not see it even with a telescope. Conditions were far from ideal, and there was too much low lying mist for my liking, but all other observers agreed that the eclipse was unusual for its darkness. There have been various earlier cases of dark eclipses following major volcanic outbreaks on Earth.

The eclipse of December 19, 1964 was excellently seen from England, particularly as—for once—the skies were cloudless over most of the country (see Plate IX). The Moon did not disappear, even at mid-totality, but it was definitely a dark eclipse, and no bright hues were seen; I could detect nothing except a rusty red sheen over part of the eclipsed disk. What struck me particularly was the emergence of the stars. Before the eclipse began, the brilliant moonlight had hidden all but the very brightest stars; as the eclipse proceeded, more and more stars came into view, and after totality I could see fifth-magnitude stars with the naked eye even within a few degrees of the Moon. Zeta Tauri, which also was close to the Moon, appeared as bright as it does on a normal moonless night. Then, as the shadow started to withdraw at the end of totality, the stars slowly faded away again. It was remarkably impressive. The small partial eclipse of 1965 (June 14) was not nearly so dark.

The following lunar eclipses will take place before the end of 1972:

1967 April 24, 12h 7m. Total. Invisible in Britain, partly visible in the U.S.A.

1967 October 18, 10h 16m. Total. Invisible in Britain, partly visible in the U.S.A.

1968 April 13, 4h 49m. Total. Partly visible in Britain, visible in the U.S.A.

1968 October 6, 11h 41m. Total. Invisible in Britain, partly visible in the U.S.A.

1970 February 21, 8h 31m. Small partial (Moon 1/20 eclipsed). Invisible in Britain, visible in the U.S.A.

1970 August 17, 3h 25m. Partial (Moon 4/10 eclipsed). Partly visible in Britain, visible in the U.S.A.

1971 February 10, 7h 42m. Total. Partly visible in Britain, visible in the U.S.A.

1971 August 6, 19h 44m. Total. Partly visible in Britain, visible in the U.S.A.

1972 January 30, 10h 53m. Total. Invisible in Britain, visible in the U.S.A.

1972 July 26, 7h 18m. Partial (Moon 6/10 eclipsed). Invisible in Britain, visible in the U.S.A.

("Partly visible" means that the Moon either rises or sets during the eclipse.)

It cannot be claimed that a lunar eclipse has anything of the grandeur of a total eclipse of the Sun, and neither is it so important astronomically, but it is fascinating none the less. Binoculars will usually bring out the colours, and even with the naked eye the slow march of the Earth's shadow across the face of the Moon cannot fail to be impressive. If the skies are really clear, it is interesting to estimate the magnitude of the faintest stars visible during totality. The brightness of the fully shadowed Moon varies considerably from eclipse to eclipse, and so the darkness of the sky varies too.

While we are dealing with what may be called celestial hide-and-seek, we must say something about occultations. As the Moon moves across the sky, it must sometimes pass in front of stars and hide them. There is no atmosphere surrounding the Moon's limb, and so a star shines steadily up to the moment when it is occulted; as the Moon sweeps in front of it, the star snaps out as abruptly as a candle-flame in the wind. When the occultation takes place at the dark limb of

Fig. 85. Occultation of a star or planet by the Moon. If the occultation takes place at the dark limb, the star may seem to be "within" the Moon —a pure optical illusion. In the diagram, the occultation will take place at the point shown.

the Moon (Fig. 85), the phenomenon is very spectacular. One moment, the star is there; the next, it has gone.

Occultations are reasonably common, but probably not so common as most people imagine, because the Moon is deceptively small in the sky. During 1964, for instance, there were only eighteen occultations of naked-eye stars, and of these stars only two (Eta and Mu Geminorum) were above magnitude $3\frac{1}{2}$.

The naked eye is not adequate to observe occultations except when the star concerned is very bright. Unfortunately the only first-magnitude stars which lie close enough to the ecliptic to be subject to occultation are Antares, Aldebaran, Pollux, Spica and Regulus. I very much doubt if the naked-eye observer would be able to follow even Aldebaran, the brightest of these, right up to the moment of occultation except under ideal conditions—that is to say, a dark-limb occultation when the Moon is a slender crescent and yet visible against a reasonably dark sky. There is, however, one optical illusion worth noting. As the Moon creeps closer and closer to the star, the unwary watcher may think that the star has moved "between the horns", so to speak, as in the Turkish flag. Binoculars bring this out well, unless the dark side of the Moon is earthlit.

Planets are occulted from time to time, and with Venus, Mars, Jupiter or Saturn the naked-eye observer can follow the complete process, but opportunities are depressingly rare. Over thirty years I have seen only two planetary occultations, both of Mars.

Occultations are still of astronomical importance, because the position of the Moon in the sky cannot be predicted with complete accuracy, and if the occultation of a star is carefully timed it is possible to deduce the exact position of the Moon at that moment. Amateurs equipped with telescopes and accurate stop-watches can do valuable work in this field. The naked-eye observer is much more limited, but he can at least enjoy the rare spectacle of a brilliant planet being blacked out by the limb of the advancing Moon.

Chapter Twenty-One

SPACE NOMADS

COMETS AND METEORS have been termed the nomads of the Sun's family. They belong to the Solar System, but they are very definitely the junior members, and many of them are short-lived on the astronomical time-scale.

Most people picture a comet as being a brilliant object, with a long tail stretching across the sky. This is a fair description of a "Great Comet", but the average comet is quite unspectacular, often tailless and too faint to be seen without a moderate telescope.

It is often thought, too, that a comet will race across the sky in a few seconds. This is quite wrong. A comet is made up of relatively small particles surrounded by an envelope of thin gas; it owes its luminosity to sunlight, and it is millions of miles away from us. It moves against the starry background, but not perceptibly, and careful measures from hour to hour are needed to show that it is moving at all. A distant comet will crawl very slowly, and will remain in much the same position in the sky for several nights in succession.

Though comets move round the Sun, their orbits are different from those of the planets. Instead of being almost circular, their paths are strongly elliptical, as shown in Fig. 86, in which the orbits of the outer planets are given together with that of the most famous periodical comet, Halley's. Halley's Comet takes 76 years to complete one journey round the Sun, and will return to perihelion, or point of closest approach, in the year 1986. At present it is still wandering beyond the orbit of Neptune, and is much too dim to be seen even with our largest telescopes. Not until 1984 is it likely to be seen again, and it will be a naked-eye object for only a few months during 1986 before it retreats once more into the depths of the Solar System.

There are various comets of shorter period; Encke's, for instance, comes to perihelion every $3\frac{1}{3}$ years, and has been seen at 48 different returns since it was originally discovered

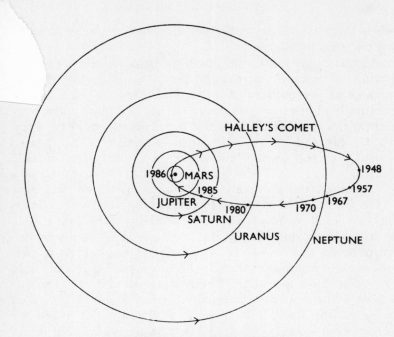

Fig. 86. Orbit of Halley's Comet.
Aphelion—1948; perihelion—1986.

in the year 1786. Several dozens of comets have periods of between 4 and 40 years, and there are others with periods of from 40 to 160 years. Yet of all these periodical comets, only Halley's is ever to be seen without optical aid—and since it will not come back into view for more than twenty years yet, there seems little point in describing it in detail here. It is so named because its orbit was first worked out by Edmond Halley, the second Astronomer Royal. Most comets, however, are named after their discoverers; thus d'Arrest's Comet (period 6¾ years) was originally found by the German astronomer Heinrich d'Arrest.

Short-period comets are predictable, and are seen regularly, but as they are too faint to be seen with the naked eye they need concern us no more at the moment. Quite different are the unexpected visitors from outer space, whose periods are measured in hundreds, thousands, or tens of thousands of years. Obviously, we cannot tell when they will appear, and when they make a dramatic entrance they are liable to catch astronomers by surprise.

A great comet must be a superb spectacle. There is a central portion or nucleus, surrounded by a "head", while the tail streams off for millions of miles. Unfortunately, the present century has been strangely poor in them. Brilliant comets were seen at intervals all through the last century—in 1811, 1843, 1858, 1861 and 1882, for instance—but none has appeared since 1910, and by the law of averages another is certainly overdue. Therefore I can give no first-hand description of a great comet, and must rely upon photographs and drawings.

On the other hand, there have been various recent comets bright enough to reach naked-eye visibility. The best-known is that of the spring of 1957, discovered simultaneously by two astronomers and known as Comet Arend-Roland. At its best it was quite prominent, and the brightest part of its tail could be seen without optical aid. Binoculars showed it well, and this was also true of an almost equally bright comet (Mrkos') seen a few months later. Both these, as well as the few naked-eye comets seen since, were classed as non-periodical. No doubt they will return to perihelion eventually, but they will be out of sight for many thousands of years before they reappear. Such was Cunningham's comet of 1940, shown in Plate X.

No useful work can be done with the naked eye so far as comets are concerned, apart possibly from estimating their magnitudes, but a comet is worth looking at even if it seems no more exciting than a patch of luminous fog; its position among the stars will change from night to night, and the careful observer will be able to plot its path across the sky. If we are lucky enough to be presented with another great comet in the near future, naked-eye studies can be made of its structure. Comets are swiftly-changing bodies, and may even develop extra tails at short notice.

Comets are utterly harmless, despite their old reputation for bringing ill-fortune. They are not hard, solid objects on the pattern of planets; they are of remarkably small mass, and according to one theory are made up mainly of "ices" together with highly rarefied gas. On more than one occasion the Earth has been known to pass through a comet's tail without suffering the slightest damage. Incidentally, a comet-tail always points more or less away from the Sun, so that on its outward journey the direction of motion is tail-first. It usually happens that a comet develops a tail only as it nears perihelion, and loses the tail again as soon as it has receded.

Associated with comets are the meteors, or shooting-stars. Here there is definite scope for the naked-eye observer, and so I propose to deal with the whole subject in rather more detail.

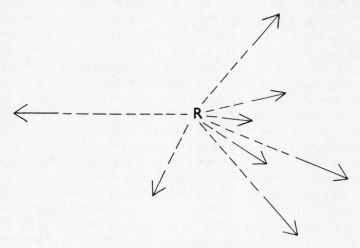

Fig. 87. Meteor radiant.

A meteor is a small particle, usually smaller than a grain of sand, moving round the Sun in an elliptical path. When well away from the Earth it is much too small to be seen, but if it approaches within 120 miles of the ground it will dash into the upper part of our atmosphere. Since it may be moving at anything up to 45 miles per second, it will rub violently against the air-particles; friction will be set up, and the meteor will become so hot that it will destroy itself in the streak of radiation that we call a shooting-star. Let it be stressed at once that that a shooting-star has nothing whatsoever to do with a real star. A star is a sun; a shooting-star is merely a tiny piece of piece of material burning away in the Earth's atmosphere. By the time it has dropped to 40 miles or so, it will have been burned away.

Meteors tend to travel round the Sun in swarms, with the

result that there are various well-defined shooting-star showers every year. Each August, for instance, the Earth passes through the swarm known as the Perseids, and meteors are plentiful; anyone who stares up at clear, dark sky for a few minutes around the end of the second week in August will be very unlucky not to see at least one shooting-star. The meteors seem to radiate from a point in the sky located in the constellation Perseus, which is why they have been so named.

The diagram in Fig. 87 shows what is meant. If plotted "backwards", all the meteors would seem to emanate from point R, which is termed the radiant of the shower. (Of course, the meteors will not be seen all at the same time; with the Perseids, the display goes on for more than a fortnight.) This does not mean that point R has any real significance. The meteors in a swarm are travelling through space in parallel paths, and their apparent divergence from a radiant is nothing more than an effect of perspective. The best everyday analogy is to picture a straight motorway, with parallel lanes. To an observer standing on a bridge over the motorway, the lanes will seem to meet at a distant point, which may be termed the radiant of the lanes. Cars travelling down the motorway will therefore seem to diverge. It is much the same with a meteor.

There are numerous annual showers, but not all of them are rich. Their intensities are measured in what is termed Z.H.R., or Zenithal Hourly Rate, which is simply the average number of meteors from the shower seen, at peak activity, when the radiant is at the zenith (overhead point). Thus if you happen to be at a site from which the radiant of the Perseid shower lies overhead on August 12, you may expect to see 50 meteors every hour, since 50 is the Z.H.R. of the Perseids. A perfectly clear, dark sky is assumed.

The main annual showers are as follows:

Name	Date			Z.H.R.	Remarks
	Beginning	Maximum	End	at max	
Quadrantids	Jan. 3	Jan. 4	Jan. 5	45	Very short, sharp maximum.
Lyrids	Apr. 19	Apr. 22	Apr. 22	10	Swift meteors.
Eta Aquarids	May 1	May 5	May 8	10	Not well seen in Britain, as the radiant is low. Swift

					meteors with long paths.
Delta Aquarids	July 15	July 29	Aug. 10	40	Not well seen in Britain, as the radiant is low. Slow meteors.
Perseids	July 27	Aug. 12	Aug. 17	50	Very rich. Swift meteors.
Orionids	Oct. 15	Oct. 21	Oct. 25	15	Swift meteors.
Taurids	Oct. 26	Nov. 1–9	Nov. 16	10	Prolonged shower. Slow meteors.
Leonids	Nov. 14	Nov. 16	Nov. 17	variable	Unpredictable shower. Very swift, bright meteors.
Bieliids	Nov. 17	Nov. 21	Nov. 27	low	Often almost imperceptible.
Geminids	Dec. 9	Dec. 13	Dec. 14	60	Very rich. Moderately swift meteors.
Ursids	Dec. 20	Dec. 22	Dec. 22	5	Radiant lies in Ursa Minor.

One or two of these names will be unfamiliar. The Quadrantids have their radiant in the part of the sky once occupied by the constellation of Quadrans Muralis (the Mural Quadrant), which has now vanished from official star-maps; the nearest bright star to the radiant position is Beta Boötis, shown in the chart on page 93. The maximum is extremely short, lasting only an hour or two, but the shower can sometimes be quite rich.

The April Lyrids are not nearly so plentiful, but the maximum lasts for longer; the radiant lies near Vega. The Eta and Delta Aquarids, from Aquarius, are good showers, but are never well seen from Europe, because when activity is at its peak the radiant is very low down in the sky. The Perseids are much the most spectacular of all the showers (even though the December Geminids may sometimes have a higher Z.H.R.), and when moonlight does not interfere the observer will be treated to a grand display of celestial fireworks. The Orionids and the Taurids call for no special mention, but the Leonids are of unusual interest.

The Leonid shower is of very variable intensity, because the main swarm is bunched together instead of being spread out all along the orbit. There used to be major displays every 33 years, and this continued right up to Victorian times; for example, there were superb showers in 1799, 1833 and 1866, when it was said that meteors "fell like rain". After 1866, unfortunately, the path of the shower was altered by the gravitational influence of Jupiter, and the Earth no longer crosses the richest part of it, so that the expected display of 1899 did not materialize. Yet there are still years when a good many Leonids are seen, as in 1961. The maximum is generally rather sharp, and there is a high proportion of very fast, bright meteors, since the shower meets the Earth "head-on". The Leonids move in the same path of Tempel's Comet, which was discovered in 1866, but which has not been seen since and has probably disintegrated.

Though the Earth now misses the main Leonid swarm by more than a million miles, the shower is still reasonably rich every 33 years, and the crucial period approached once more in 1964. The maximum was expected late on the night of November 16–17, and it seemed worth making a special effort to cover it. Accordingly, I went on B.B.C. Television, together with H. B. Ridley (Director of the Meteor Section of the British Astronomical Association) and appealed for volunteer watchers. The results were highly encouraging, and we had many dozens of reports from people who had stayed up in the early hours of a winter morning to see what was to be seen. The weather was bad over most of England, but things were somewhat better in Scotland, and we were able to establish that the Z.H.R. of the 1964 Leonids was between 30 and 50, probably nearer 50. This was a case in which naked-eye observers, many of them totally inexperienced, were able to make a valuable contribution to meteor study. One of the charts sent in, made by Colin Jack in Fifeshire, is given here (Fig. 88), and it will be seen that the radiant is well indicated. The meteor to the left-hand side of the chart, making a considerable angle with the rest, is probably unconnected with the Leonid shower.

It remains to be seen what the Leonids will do in the coming years, but it is always worth keeping a close watch for a night

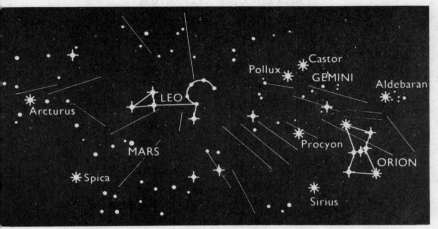

Fig. 88. The Radiant of the 1964 Leonids, as determined by naked-eye observations by Colin Jack, at Drumairlie in Fifeshire, Scotland. It will be seen that the trails indicate a well-defined radiant in Leo; the few meteors moving at sharp angles are almost certainly sporadic, and not true members of the Leonid shower.

or two around November 16.

The Bieliids are equally intriguing. Their radiant lies in the constellation Andromeda, and they are often known as the Andromedids. Again there is a cometary association, this time with Biela's Comet, which used to move round the Sun in a period of 6¾ years. At the return of 1846 it split in half, causing marked consternation in astronomical circles. The twin comets were seen again in 1852, but this was their last appearance—*as* comets. They were missed in 1858, probably because of their unfavourable position in the sky, but they should have been seen in 1866; yet no trace of them was found. At the next predicted return, that of 1872, the comet was again absent, but a rich shower of meteors took its place. Since then the shower has declined, and often it cannot be identified at all, but a few Bieliids are usually to be seen between November 17 and 27, and here too there is every reason to maintain a close watch. It would be an over-simplification to suppose that Biela's Comet broke up into meteors, but the connection between the shooting-star shower and the dead comet cannot be questioned.

A Z.H.R. figure can be somewhat misleading, since in

Britain and the United States, at least, shower radiants will never lie exactly on the zenith. A correction must always be made, according to a table worked out by the leading British meteor observer J. P. M. Prentice. First, the altitude of the radiant must be estimated. The observed hourly rate must then be multiplied by the correction factor to give the true Z.H.R..

Altitude of radiant, degrees	Correction factor	Altitude of radiant, degrees	Correction factor
90	1	27	2
66	1·1	20	2·5
52	1·25	14	3·3
42	1·4	9	5
35	1·6	2·5	10

These figures are only approximate, and Prentice has given them to a greater degree of accuracy, but they will serve as a good guide. For instance, suppose that you observe for a full hour and find that you have seen 14 meteors: what is the Z.H.R.? Check the position of the radiant; let us say that it has an altitude of 60 degrees. From the table, the correction factor falls somewhere between 1·1 and 1·25; take this as 1·2. $14 \times 1·2 = 16·8$, which is the true Z.H.R., though in practice the figure would be rounded off to 17. Of course, things are more complicated if the sky is hazy or moonlit, or not properly dark, since the calculated Z.H.R. is then bound to be much too low.

Generally speaking, the most useful work now available to the naked-eye observer is to find out the Z.H.R.'s of the various showers, as we did with the 1964 Leonids. Beware of "sporadic" meteors, which may appear from any direction at any time, and which have no connection with definite showers. Sorting out the sporadics is largely a matter of common-sense, but they are not nearly so numerous as might be thought. Meteors tend to be gregarious.

The altitude of the radiant changes from hour to hour, and so the correction factor alters too. It is hopeless to expect a high hourly rate when the radiant is low; not only will some of the meteors be below the horizon, but the fainter ones will be lost in low-lying haze or mist. The Leonids, for example, are observable only during the early hours of the morning, since in November the radiant does not rise until about midnight.

Up to the end of the war, most of our knowledge of meteor heights and speeds was due to amateur work. The observer plotted the path of the meteor against the stars; no equipment was needed apart from a reliable watch, a piece of stick or cord, and a star atlas. The method was to note the duration and time of the meteor, and then hold up the stick against the part of the sky across which it had flashed; the starting and ending points could then be estimated, and either plotted on the star-map or else recorded with respect to convenient stars.

If the same meteor were observed by two or three watchers, separated by several miles, the real path of the meteor through the atmosphere could be worked out. This was done frequently, and with good results, so that amateur meteor enthusiasts were in great demand. Then, after 1945, new and much more technical methods were developed, involving radar principles, so that the old visual path-plotting became more or less obsolete. It is still interesting to do, and the observer can work out his own radiants if he sees enough meteors, but its scientific value has been undeniably reduced. On the other hand, it is valuable to note meteor magnitudes, colours and trails, remembering that no colour is likely to be seen in any meteor below zero magnitude.

An exceptionally brilliant meteor is usually called a fireball, though the name is not a suitable one. Fireballs are almost always sporadic (that is to say, unconnected with any shower) and are rather larger than rank-and-file meteors, sometimes attaining the majestic size of a ball-bearing. They are rare, but not exceptionally so. During the past thirty years I have seen at least a dozen fireballs which have outshone Venus, and one which rivalled the full moon. When a fireball is seen, plot the path as accurately as possible, and note down all details such as date, time, duration, magnitude, colour, rate of movement, and any visible trail.[1]

[1] There is no strict definition of the term "fireball". It is usually held to apply to any meteor brighter than Venus, but other observers restrict it to objects comparable with the Moon.

To sum up: the present-day visual observer has definite scope, principally in studying the various showers and estimating their Z.H.R. values. Meteor photography is more useful still, and any amateur enthusiast can undertake it, but to deal with it here would be beyond my scope.[1]

Larger objects, big enough to survive the complete drop through the atmosphere without being destroyed, are termed meteorites. They differ from ordinary shooting-star meteors, and seem to be more nearly related to the asteroids. Most museums have collections of them, but the largest known meteorite is still lying where it fell in prehistoric times at Hoba West, Africa; I doubt whether anyone will try to run away with it, since it weighs at least sixty tons. The largest meteorite in captivity, so to speak, is the 36-ton Greenland monster discovered by the explorer Peary, now on view at the Hayden Planetarium in New York.

The average meteorite is very much smaller than this, and is made up either of stony material or else of iron. No meteorite has been linked with a shooting-star shower, which adds force to the argument that the two types of objects are entirely distinct; if you go out on an August evening to look for Perseids, you need have no fear of being hit on the head by a piece of falling stone, and in fact there is no authenticated case of anyone having been killed by a meteorite. Really major falls are excessively rare, and in recorded times there have been only two, one in 1908 and the other in 1947, both in Siberia. The famous Meteor Crater in Arizona was undoubtedly formed by a missile from outer space, but is prehistoric.

There have been a few cases of meteorites being observed during their passage through the atmosphere, and one or two have even been located because amateur reports have enabled their impact-points to be tracked. Unfortunately, the chances that any reader of this book will ever see a falling meteorite are so low that I do not propose to dwell upon the subject. In sheer self-defence, however, let me add that it is often hard to tell a meteorite from a non-meteorite. Some years ago I described meteorites during the course of one of my monthly

[1] For a full discussion, see H. B. Ridley's chapter in *Practical Amateur Astronomy* (Lutterworth Press, London 1964).

television programmes on astronomy, with dire results. During the next few weeks I was inundated with pieces of material of all shapes and sizes; they arrived by every post, some of them in vast cases, together with letters saying, in various assorted ways, "Is this a meteorite? And if so, what is it worth?" Not one "meteorite" was genuine, but the collection included an impressive selection of minerals as well as bizarre specimens such as a piece of anchor, several slabs of cork matting, a couple of cannonballs and a very old Bath bun. By the time I had returned them all to their rightful owners, my enthusiasm for meteoritics was slightly dampened.

Meteor-watching is a cold business, and it requires considerable patience, particularly when the observer is waiting for a very weak shower such as the Bieliids or the Leonids in one of their off-moments. Yet it is worth doing, and the enthusiast who begins some serious naked-eye watching may eventually become keen enough to take up meteor photography, where he can contribute results of real scientific value.

Chapter Twenty-Two

GLOWS IN THE SKY

ON THE MORNING of January 26, 1938, when the world was still in a state of uneasy peace, the daily newspapers in Britain were full of an event which was quite non-political. "Weirdest Storm over London," ran one headline. "Sky Glows Fiery Red." There followed a long description of what many people had taken to be the glare of a great fire, but which had in fact been a particularly brilliant display of Northern Lights. For once, Hitler and Mussolini were relegated to the back pages.

I watched that display of aurora from my Sussex home, and even now it remains vividly in my mind, though from Iceland and the northern part of Canada I have seen even more spectacular auroræ since. It is quite true that the sky turned red, but there were arches, glowing curtains and streamers as well, shifting and changing all the time that the display lasted. Nobody who was outdoors at the time can have failed to have been impressed.

Auroræ have been known for centuries, but the name dates only from 1621, when the French scientist Gassendi first coined it. To be strictly accurate, the modern term is "Aurora Polaris", or Polar Light—in northern latitudes, Aurora Borealis; in southern, Aurora Australis. The wonderful Lights are seldom seen from anywhere near the equator, for reasons which are obvious enough when we realize the way in which they are produced.

Though auroræ occur inside the Earth's atmosphere, at heights ranging from below 70 miles up to as much as 500 miles, they are certainly the business of the astronomer, because their origin lies in the Sun. The exact mechanism is not yet understood, but the main principles are definite enough.

The Sun sends out streams of charged particles, which move at speeds of around 600 miles per second, and often reach the Earth. When they do so, they smash into the upper air and bombard the atoms and molecules there, so causing a glow; the process is not unlike that which occurs in mercury and sodium discharge tubes used in many of the street lamps which are such a bane to astronomers. Complications are introduced by the Van Allen radiation belts which surround the Earth, and which were discovered quite unexpectedly as a result of measures carried out by instruments aboard the first successful American artificial satellite, Explorer I, sent aloft in 1958. The influence of the Van Allen particles upon auroræ is still a matter for debate, but there is a very close link.

Since the particles from the Sun are electrically charged, they are affected by the Earth's magnetic field, which is why auroræ are best seen from high latitudes. The geographical poles have nothing directly to do with it; it is the magnetic poles which matter. Anyone who wants to see auroræ to advantage would be well advised to go not to the North or South Pole, but to the latitude of Iceland, Northern Norway, or the Antarctic coast. During the long Icelandic winter nights it is seldom that any clear sky is free from aurora, though the Londoner or New Yorker may go for years without seeing a single bright display.

The Sun, as we have noted, is in some respects variable, following a roughly regular 11-year cycle of activity. Near maximum there are frequent sunspots, together with the short-short-lived, violent outbursts which are known as flares, and which are basically electrical in character. Flares are particularly associated with the emission of charged particles, and hence they are also associated with auroræ, to say nothing of other less welcome phenomena such as radio fade-outs. This is not to say that every flare produces an aurora; there is no hard and fast rule, but at any event auroræ are much more common near the time of solar maximum.

Any brief examination of past records will prove this. All major displays away from the main auroral zone take place near peak sunspot and flare activity, and few or none will be seen near solar minimum, though inconspicuous glows over the horizon may sometimes be distinguished by experienced watchers. For instance, activity on the Sun was at a low ebb during 1963 and 1964, and from Sussex I failed to see any trace of aurora. By 1969–70 things should have become much more interesting again.

The horizon glows seen from England and places along

similar latitudes are nothing more than the upper parts of auroral displays which are overhead in or near the main zones; it is only during periods of activity on the Sun that the auroræ "move south", so to speak, and produce spectacular effects over Britain and the northern United States. At the same time the aurora australis extends north, but this does not help much, since it seldom spreads as far as the nearest thickly-populated lands. Generally speaking, the Southern Lights waste their beauty upon desolate oceans.

There are several distinct types of auroræ. First, there is the general horizon glow, which is none too easy to identify; many an observer has reported an "aurora" which has proved to be nothing more than the glow of a distant town. If, of course, the light extends upward from the horizon to form a quiet arc, there is no longer any doubt about its nature. If the display is a major one, the arc may then send up rays at right-angles to its length, while the arc itself folds to form an irregular band. If the rays are really long, the band starts to give the impression of what is termed drapery, while it is also possible for the rays to converge to a point at the zenith, forming an auroral corona (not to be confused with the Sun's corona). Waves of light may surge up from the horizon, causing parts of the aurora to brighten in turn; this so-called flaming aurora is really glorious, though rare except in high latitudes. Also, there may be a general sky-glow or veil, as well as diffuse isolated patches.

It is not easy to explain the various auroral forms by mere written description, particularly as no two displays are exactly alike. Meanwhile, what are the methods of observation?

Here, for once, we find that telescopes are quite useless, and binoculars are of limited value, though they can sometimes be of value in identifying stars so that the positions of the auroral forms can be plotted. Photographic work is possible, but has its limitations, because auroræ change so rapidly. All in all, the naked eye is much the best instrument for work in this field, and nothing else is needed except for some rough measuring device. A foot-rule held at arm's length will give a scale of one degree to the half-inch, and this is usually good enough, though an elaborate quadrant can be made by anyone with enough practical skill. (I find it helpful to remember that the distance between the Pointers in the Great Bear is 5 degrees, while Polaris to Beta Cassiopeiæ is 30 degrees.)

Naked-eye observation of aururæ by amateurs is most valuable, and negative evidence is always important. The systematic observer should always record a note whenever he makes a check and finds that aurora is absent. When a display is seen, the form and position should be written down; the position angle should be given in degrees, starting at zero for north and working round to east (90°), south (180°) and west (270°) back to north. Together with the altitude, this will fix the position of the auroral form, but it is often sufficient to do no more than mark it against the background of the constellations. Serious observers have special recording symbols, but most people will be content to gaze at the aurora when it appears, enjoying its beauty and its rapid changes of shape and brilliance.

Unfortunately, Britons and dwellers in the United States are at a grave disadvantage, partly because auroræ are comparatively uncommon and partly (with England) because there are so many artificial lights around. The presence of a town in an awkward direction will conceal the horizon glows, and I very much doubt whether anyone who lives in Central London or New York will see more than one aurora in fifty years. The advance of what we sardonically call "civilization" is making things steadily worse for the auroral observer. Before the war I could see quite a number of auroræ each year from my Sussex home, around the time of solar maximum, but nowadays the sky is not so dark, and all but the brightest auroræ are effectively drowned. Matters are better in Scotland, and from Caithness or Sutherland there is plenty of scope. North Canada, too, is an excellent site. I have seen some really splendid displays from the Hudson's Bay region.

Before leaving the aurora, I should not omit to mention the peculiar crackles reported from time to time. There is no obvious reason why an aurora should be noisy, and I admit to having doubts about it; in my experience, auroræ have always been blissfully silent. Any so-called auroral sounds will probably be found to be due to local activity, quite unconnected with what is happening in the sky. All the same, odd phenomena of this sort should always be checked.

Quite different from the aurora is the faint, ghostly glow known as the Zodiacal Light. Here we are dealing with something which is purely astronomical, since the Light is due to countless tiny particles spread out in the main plane of the Solar System and lit up by the Sun. The layer of particles cannot be very broad, since the Zodiacal Light is confined to the region of the ecliptic. Near the horizon, the width of the main cone may be as much as 25 degrees, but it tapers quickly, and becomes comparatively narrow as it recedes from the Sun. Its name is appropriate enough, since it keeps strictly to the belt marking the Zodiac—in which the planets are also to be found.

The Zodiacal Light is not easy to observe from England or the northern United States. It is not affected by magnetic forces, but the Light is much fainter than even a moderate aurora, and it is never visible until the sky is dark. Neither can it be seen late at night, since by then the Sun has dropped well below the horizon, and the Zodiacal Light has also set. It has to be glimpsed at the most favourable moments, and, to make things worse, moonlight will hide it completely.

From Europe, the best chances of seeing the Light occur when the ecliptic is most nearly perpendicular to the horizon. When the ecliptic makes a sharp angle with the horizon, the Zodical Light is low down, so that it will shine through relatively dense layers of atmosphere and will probably not be seen at all. So far as Britain is concerned, the best moments occur in early March, but it is sometimes possible to see the Light on any clear, dark evening between mid-February and the last week in March; for morning observation, the corresponding time is between mid-September and late October.

Conditions are more favourable from countries near the equator, because the skies are clearer and twilight is much shorter. I have never been to the tropics, but I have spoken to many people who have recorded the Zodiacal Light as being much brighter than the Milky Way.

For observing the Zodiacal Light, no instruments of any sort are needed apart from a foot-rule, a star-map, a notebook and a pencil. The procedure is to record the width of the base in degrees, remembering that at arm's length one degree is about half an inch on the ruler; estimate the position of the top of the cone, in degrees above the horizon; plot the cone itself on a star-map as accurately as possible, and give the intensity of the Light in terms of various parts of the Milky Way. It is important to gauge the transparency of the sky, which can best be done by noting the faintest stars visible without optical aid and then checking on their magnitudes.

Some observers have found that the main cone has definite structure, with an inner core surrounded to either side by fainter flanks. I have never seen this myself, but people with keener eyes than mine should be more successful. Neither have I been able to make out the slightly pinkish hue of the brightest region which has been described on various occasions.

One point stands out at once: if you are going to make useful records of the Zodiacal Light, you must have a really good working knowledge of the constellations, so that the position of the dim cone can be checked. It is useless to say that "the apex stretches up to a fairly bright star with a fainter one beside it". If you can say "The apex lies mid-way between Zeta and Beta Tauri", the position can be plotted with sufficient accuracy.

There are two other glows, probably of the same basic nature as the Zodiacal Light but even more elusive. One is the Zodiacal Band, a parallel beam of extremely faint and diffused light stretching across the sky, making up what is in effect an extension of the main cone. It is nothing like so bright as the Milky Way, and in fact it cannot be seen at all if it happens to lie near the Milky Way area; the slightest trace of mist, or any moonlight, will conceal it. I have to confess that I have yet to see it properly.

I have, however, made on definite observation of the mysterious Gegenschein or Counterglow, which makes up the brightest part of the Zodiacal Band. It was first described by the Danish astronomer Theodor Brorsen more than a century ago, and has often been recorded, but nobody is quite sure of its precise nature; all we can say is that it lies well beyond the top of the atmosphere, and is probably due to thinly-spread material in the plane of the Solar System. It is seen exactly opposite to the Sun in the sky, and on occasion may cover an area as large as that of the Square of Pegasus. From all available evidence it is at its best in September and early October, but even then it is excessively fugitive.

My one observation of it was made in 1941, when Britain was blacked out and conditions for observation were excellent—even though people such as myself were in no position to take advantage of them! I have often looked for the Gegenschein since, but with no result. Absolute darkness and clarity are essential.

It should be borne in mind, too, that the human eye is slow to adapt itself. There is no point in walking outside from a brightly-lit room and expecting to see faint glows (or, for that matter, faint stars). The observer must stay in darkness for some time, probably as much as twenty minutes, before his eyes will be ready for such work. Beware, too, of the familiar pocket torch. As soon as you switch on a light in order to record your notes, the dark-adaptation process will have to be started all over again. The only solution is to have a very dim torch, preferably with a red bulb; even this should be used as sparingly as is practicable.

There are various other sky-glows, but it is difficult to decide whether they should be included here, since anything inside the atmosphere is meteorological rather than astronomical (excluding the aurora, which has a purely astronomical origin). Still, perhaps it will be as well to say something about them, even if it means invading the weather-man's province.

Rainbows, of course, are very familiar, and touch the ground at times. A rainbow is caused by raindrops in the air, which split up the Sun's light; usually there are two bows, a primary and a secondary. In the primary, red is seen at the outer part of the band, with violet inwards and various other colours between; in the fainter secondary, the red is on the inside. Obviously, a rainbow is visible exactly opposite the Sun, and is a clear sign of showery weather.

It is not so generally known that the Moon can also cause rainbows, though the bright hues are lacking. I once saw an excellent lunar rainbow when flying over North Scotland during the early part of the war, but I was unable to devote much attention to it, for the excellent reason that I was navigating the aircraft and had no particular desire to find myself over Cologne instead of Caithness. I have never been lucky enough to see another.

A Sun Pillar is due to the reflection of the Sun's rays from the vertical sides of a column of crystals in the atmosphere. It looks like a pillar of red or white light extending vertically above and below the Sun, sometimes crossed by a similar horizontal bar making up what is popularly called a Heavenly Cross. Moon pillars are also known. Here also I must rely upon the eye-witness accounts of others, since solar and lunar pillars are uncommon, but at least I have seen plenty of haloes.

A halo is produced when the Sun or Moon shines through a very thin layer of cloud of the type known as cirrostratus, which forms a veil over the entire sky and is made up of ice crystals at over 20,000 feet above the ground. The cloud itself is more or less transparent, and the casual observer may not realize that it is present, but it is responsible for haloes, which appear as faint rings surrounding the Sun or Moon. Colours are not conspicuous, but there may be a red tint on the inner edge of the halo together with a yellow caste on the outer part. Cirrostratus cloud is often the forerunner of rain, and so a halo too is a sign of probable bad weather ahead.

Different again is a corona, not to be confused with the Sun's true corona as seen during a total eclipse, or with an auroral corona. It is associated with lower clouds of the alto-cumulus type, and is due to the diffraction of light-rays by water-particles inside the cloud. It is smaller than a halo, and is not necessarily a signal of approaching rain. Lunar coronæ are quite spectacular at times, but in the ordinary way a corona round the Sun cannot be seen without the use of a dark filter, so that few people will know that it is there.

Parhelia, or mock-suns, are more intriguing. When the weather is very cold, and ice-crystals are present in the lower portion of the atmosphere, refraction effects produce false images of the Sun, often connected by luminous rays. Mock-moons are similar, but less striking. Parhelia are best seen from the polar zones, and are extremely rare over Britain or the United States. I have never seen one myself.

Finally, let us note that blue suns and blue moons do occur

sometimes, when the upper air contains an unusual quantity of dust or ash. I have seen several, the most impressive being that of September 26, 1950, when from East Grinstead in Sussex the Moon was a lovely, shimmering blue. In this case, the cause was upper-atmosphere dust produced by gigantic forest fires raging in Canada. The tremendous volcanic eruption of Krakatoa in 1883 is said to have produced a host of coloured moons and suns, together with peculiar sunset effects, and there was a much more recent case of a blue sun— in 1964—which led to considerable correspondence in the English press.

With the true astronomical glows, city-dwellers are at a hopeless disadvantage, but anyone who is able to drive well out into the country where conditions are favourable has the chance to do some really useful work. The morning Zodiacal Light, for instance, has not been studied as closely as astronomers could wish; it takes a good deal of moral toughness to get up well before dawn in order to look for a glow which may well prove to be an absentee after all. Yet if you are fortunate enough to catch sight of the dim, tapering cone stretching from the horizon up into the blackness of the sky, you will feel amply rewarded. The Zodiacal Light is the reverse of spectacular, but it has a faint, eerie beauty all its own.

Chapter Twenty-Three

MOONS MADE BY MAN

IT IS A very long time since any natural planets were formed in the Solar System. The Earth itself is about 4,700 million years old, and there is no reason to think that any of its companions are much younger. Yet during the past decade there have been various additions to the sky, put there by the ingenuity of man.

The first artificial satellite, or man-made moon, was launched by the Russians on October 4, 1957. Their success was quite unexpected in the West, and it would be idle to pretend that everybody was pleased; military planners had to face up to the fact that in technology, the Soviet Union had nothing to learn from either Britain or America. Scientists took a more honourable view, and acclaimed the Russian "Sputnik I" as a major triumph—as indeed it was.

October 4, 1957, may be said to mark the opening of the Space Age, and as Sputnik I sped round the Earth, sending out the famous "Bleep! bleep!" signals from its transmitter, the whole outlook of nations toward interplanetary travel underwent a sudden change. True, the United States space-researchers had made a previous announcement about sending up a satellite, but only when Sputnik I had been sent on its way did the general public realize that the prophets of earlier years had been something more than vague dreamers and cranks.

Since then many artificial satellites have been sent up, to say nothing of rocket probes to the Moon, Venus and Mars. Their uses have been many. Some satellites have carried instruments to study the radiation belts surrounding the Earth; some have been designed to investigate radiations and particles coming from deep space; some have been concerned with the study of weather, since meteorologists are anxious to find out more about the atmosphere as a whole. There have been communications satellites, active and passive; there have been satellites carrying human crews. Various satellites have been visible with the naked eye, looking like slowly-moving stars creeping among the constellations.

As soon as an artificial satellite has been taken up by means of rocket power, and launched into an orbit round the Earth, it behaves in precisely the same way as an ordinary astronomical body. If it keeps above the top of the resisting atmosphere it will not fall down, any more than the real Moon will do. If, however, it spends any part of its orbit inside the denser layers of the Earth's air, it will be affected by friction against the air-particles, and eventually it will come down, burning up in the same way as a meteor. This was the fate which overtook Sputnik I and many of its successors. Other satellites (such as Early Bird) are so high above the ground that they are, to all intents and purposes, permanent.

Obviously, the lower-down a satellite may be, the faster it will seem to move across the sky. It may travel in almost any direction, depending upon the orbit into which its makers have sent it. Thus Echo II, the brightest satellite launched up to mid-1965, moved in a path which carried it roughly over both poles, so that it tended to travel in a north-south direction in the sky, taking some minutes to cross from one horizon to the other; its trail is shown in Plate XII. (Echo II, by the way, was a very large plastic balloon, coated with a thin layer of reflective material. It was a passive communications satellite—that is to say, radio waves transmitted from Earth were bounced off it. After a while it was punctured by meteors, and since it was rotating all the time its distorted figure made it seem to jerk along instead of moving smoothly.)

No satellite will look anything but a point of light. It cannot survive for long if it comes down below 150 miles or so, because of friction against the air, so that any satellite showing a disk to the naked eye would have to be tremendously large. In fact, there are only two ways to tell a satellite from a star. It will be an intruder, so that anyone who knows the constellations will identify it almost at once—though even experienced watchers may be deceived for a few moments, particularly if the sky is partly cloud-covered and the full star-patterns do not show up. Secondly, the satellite will have perceptible motion, which makes it betray itself almost at once. During a crossing of the sky, a satellite may pass into the Earth's shadow, so that it will be eclipsed and will vanish unceremoniously from sight.

Modern satellites are tracked by radio, radar and other means, but visual work is not to be despised, and accurate observations of naked-eye satellites are useful. Even now, our knowledge of the density of the upper air is not so complete as we could wish, and there are various other factors to be taken into account as well, so that the orbits of satellites cannot be forecast with 100 per cent precision. The only way to check on what the satellite is doing is to fix its position against the background of stars.

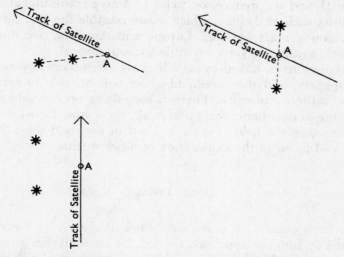

Fig. 89. In each case, the moment when the satellite reaches point A can be estimated. Of course, the stars used as references must be correctly identified!

The method is to use a stop-watch, starting it at the moment when a satellite passes close to a known star or else passes between two stars which are near each other (Fig. 89). Then, as quickly as possible, obtain a time-signal—dialling TIM on the telephone is the easiest way—and stop the watch. Suppose that you stop the watch at 20h. 11m. 51·7s. G.M.T., and find that the reading is 1m. 20·0s. This means that the satellite fix was obtained in 1m. 20·0s. ago—that is to say, at 20h. 10m. 31·7s. G.M.T.

A careless or faulty observation is worse than useless, since it may lead to confusion if it is sent in as a proper estimate. Therefore, the stop-watch must be checked frequently to make sure that it is keeping good time. In addition, the observer must have a first-class knowledge of the constellations, since he must make use of any stars which happen to lie in the track of the moving satellite, and he must know which star is which. It is not helpful to record a satellite as close to, say, Zeta Virginis when it is actually passing by Delta Leonis.

Most of the current satellites are too faint to be seen with the naked eye, but there are some notable exceptions, such as Echo II and its predecessor Echo I. Active communications satellites such as Telstar, which made possible the first direct television contact between Europe and America, are much smaller, so that they are invisible without optical aid.

Predictions for naked-eye satellites are given daily in various newspapers, and the careful observer will be able to locate them without difficulty. There is something remarkably fascinating about them; they, above all, show how far we have advanced in the field of science. Used in the right way, they can lead us on to the exploration of other worlds.

CONCLUSION

It is thousands of years now since the early star-gazers looked up into the night sky, formed the constellation groups, and began to think about what the universe might be. Nowadays astronomy has become an exact science; huge telescopes peer into space, metal "dishes" collect radio waves coming from immense distances, and rockets have been sent to our neighbour planets. Yet the magic of the night sky is unaltered, and can never be changed. To take a real interest in what is happening above, you need nothing more than your eyes, some common-sense, and sufficient patience. I hope that what I have written in this book will show that astronomy is open to us all.

Appendix I

NAKED-EYE VARIABLE STARS

THE METHOD USED to estimate the magnitude of a variable star has been explained on page 42. It is essential to select comparison stars which are as close as possible to the variable in both position and magnitude, but this is not always easy, and in some cases (Betelgeux, for instance) extinction has always to be allowed for. It is useless to make a straight comparison between, say, Betelgeux and Rigel, since to northern observers Rigel will always be much the lower of the two.

In the notes and charts which follow, intended mainly for comparatively serious observers who intend to follow up particular stars and produce light-curves, I have given the magnitudes of comparison stars to a hundredth of a magnitude, but it must be borne in mind that a naked-eye estimate can never be accurate to within more than a tenth of a magnitude at most. I have never been sure of the exact limit, but I am confident that a difference of 0·1 magnitude is detectable without instruments. Look, for example, at Orion's belt. Epsilon Orionis, the centre star, is of magnitude 1·70; Zeta is 1·79. To me, at least, Epsilon always seems perceptibly the brighter of the two, though I am not keen-sighted; neither am I a regular observer of variable stars, though I have made a good many estimates over the past thirty years or so.

The most interesting objects to the naked-eye watcher are the semi-regular and irregular variables. Few long-period stars are ever visible without optical aid, though Mira Ceti is an honourable exception.

(a) Known Variables

ETA AQUILÆ

A Cepheid, ranging from 3·7 to 4·5 in a period of 7·18 days. It is extremely easy to observe.

Comparisons: Theta Aquilæ (3·31), Delta Aquilæ (3·38), Beta Aquilæ (3·90), Theta Serpentis (4·16—the combined

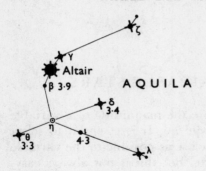

AQUILA

magnitude of the components of this wide double), and Iota Aquilæ (4·28).

Fig. 90. η Aquilæ.

EPSILON AURIGÆ

An eclipsing binary, with a period of 9,886 days or about 27 years! It is an extraordinary system, described in the text (p. 71), made up of a highly luminous supergiant (60,000 Sun-power) together with an immense tenuous companion which cannot be seen, but which is the largest individual star known. For long periods Epsilon Aurigæ remains constant, but if it seems appreciably fainter than its neighbour Eta you may be sure that eclipse is in progress.

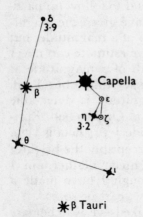

Fig. 91. ε and ζ Aurigæ.

Comparison: Eta Aurigæ (3·17). The third member of the small triangle close to Capella is Zeta Aurigæ, which is an eclipsing binary of the same general type as Epsilon. Its fluctuations are too slight to be well followed with the naked eye, particularly as the mean magnitude is only 3·9, but it cannot be used as a comparison. The official range of Epsilon itself is 3·0 to 3·8.

ALPHA CASSIOPEIÆ

There seems little doubt that the leader of the famous W is an irregular variable, though occasional doubts have been expressed. The average magnitude is about 2·2; the range

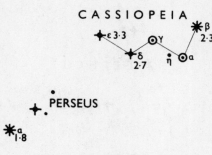

Fig. 92. *a* and *γ* Cassiopeiæ.

has been given as 2·1 to 2·8, though I consider it unlikely that the star ever drops much below 2·5. It should be carefully watched, and is easy to observe, since it is circumpolar in Britain and there are excellent comparison stars to hand.

Comparisons: Beta Cassiopeiæ (2·26), Delta Cassiopeiæ (2·67). Polaris may also be used, and taken as 2·0, though it is in fact itself variable over a very small range (1·99 to 2·10).

GAMMA CASSIOPEIÆ

A most peculiar star, subject to occasional "bursts" which send it up from its usual brilliance, well below the second magnitude, to about 1½. The probable range is 1·6 to 3·2, but the changes, like those of Alpha, are very slow except during an outburst. Gamma Cassiopeiæ is worthy of special attention, since one never knows when it is going to do something unexpected.

Comparisons: The stars used for Alpha, plus Epsilon Cassiopeiæ (3·33) and Alpha Persei (1·80). Avoid comparing Gamma and Alpha, for obvious reasons, since both are variable!

DELTA CEPHEI

The prototype Cepheid; range 3·51 to 4·42, period 5·37 days. It is always worth watching, in view of its tremendous influence upon astrophysical theories.

Comparisons: all in Cepheus—Zeta (3·31), Iota (3·68), Epsilon (4·23) and Nu (4·46).

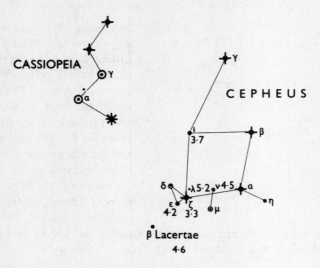

CASSIOPEIA

CEPHEUS

ι
3·7

β

δ   ·λ5·2 ·ν4·5   ·α
ε   ·ζ   ·η
4·2 3·3 ·μ

β Lacertae
4·6

Fig. 93. δ and μ Cephei.

MU CEPHEI

A red irregular of the Betelgeux type, called by Herschel "the Garnet Star". The range is from about 3·7 to 5·7, so that near minimum the star is difficult to see with the naked eye; binoculars are most helpful.

Comparisons: Lambda Cephei (5·19), Nu Cephei (4·46). I have also used Beta Lacertæ (4·60).

OMICRON CETI (MIRA)

Mira is one of the best-known of all variable stars, but it is certainly not the easiest to study. It is red, with a period averaging 331 days. Its range is from 2 to 9, so that it is visible to the naked eye only when fairly near maximum; near minimum, even binoculars and small telescopes will not show it. At some maxima, the magnitude never rises above 4.

Comparisons: Alpha Arietis (2·00), Alpha Ceti (2·54), Gamma Ceti (3·58), Delta Ceti (4·04), Zeta Ceti (3·92), Alpha Piscium (3·94).

232

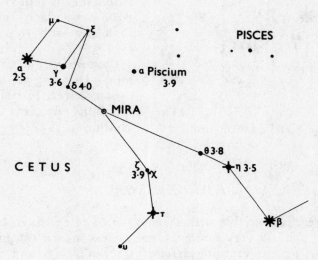

Fig. 94. *o* Ceti.

CHI CYGNI

Another red long-period variable, this time with a period averaging 409 days. The maximum magnitude may rise to above $4\frac{1}{2}$, and is given officially as 4·2, but at minimum the star becomes extremely faint— below magnitude 13. It is a naked-eye object for only a short time to either side of maximum. Eta makes an ideal comparison.

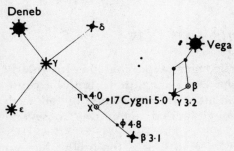

Fig. 95. χ Cygni.

Comparisons: Eta Cygni (4·03), Phi Cygni (4·79).

ZETA GEMINORUM

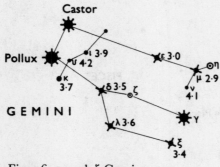

Fig. 96. η and ζ Geminorum.

A Cepheid, ranging between 3·7 and 4·3 in a period of 10·2 days. It is not a particularly easy star to follow with the naked eye.

Comparisons: all in Gemini—Delta (3·51, rather inconveniently bright), Lambda (3·65), Iota (3·89), Upsilon (4·22).

ETA GEMINORUM

A reddish variable with a mean period of 231 days. Unlike Mira, it has a very limited range of less than a magnitude, 3·3 to 4·2, so that its changes are both slow and slight. However, it is worth watching, since it seems to have received little attention in the past.

Comparisons: all in Gemini—Mu (2·92), Delta (3·51), Xi (3·38), Lambda (3·65), Kappa (3·68), Nu (4·06). Beware of Zeta, which is a Cepheid variable.

ALPHA HERCULIS

A red supergiant of the Betelgeux type, changing irregularly between 3·1 and 3·9. The exact magnitude limits are uncertain, and for this reason alone the star should be followed. There may be a very rough period amounting to several years.

Comparisons: Beta Herculis (2·78; rather too bright, but not to be despised when Alpha is at maximum), Delta Herculis (3·14), Kappa Ophiuchi (3·18), Mu Herculis (3·42), Gamma Herculis (3·79), Lambda Ophiuchi (3·85).

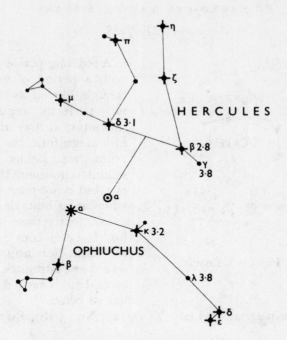

Fig. 97. *a* Herculis.

U HYDRÆ

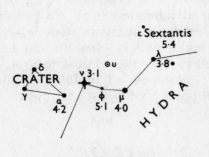

Fig. 98. *v* Hydræ.

A very difficult naked-eye star. Its range is from 4·5 to 6, and it is apparently irregular. Opportunities for seeing it without optical aid from Britain are rare, even when it is at its brightest, because of its low altitude. It is extremely red, and is a lovely sight in a pair of binoculars or any telescope.

Comparisons: Mu Hydræ (4·06), Phi Hydræ (5·11), Epsilon Sextantis (5·40).

235

R LEONIS

A red long-period variable with a period of 312 days, though, like all its kind, it is not perfectly regular. At maximum it may attain the fifth magnitude, but at minimum drops below 10. It is seldom visible with the naked eye, but is not hard to locate when at its best, since it lies conveniently close to Regulus. It is, of course, always too faint for any reliable naked-eye estimates, and optopical aid is needed to bring out its colour.

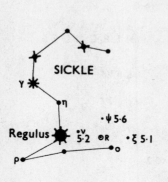

Fig. 99. κ Leonis.

Comparisons: all in Leo—Xi (5·12), Nu (5·18), Psi (5·62).

DELTA LIBRÆ

An Algol-type eclipsing binary; period 2·33 days. It is visible to the naked eye at maximum (4·8), but not at minimum (6·2). No proper naked-eye estimates are possible, and to make matters worse the star lies well south of the celestial equator.

Fig. 100. δ Libræ.

Comparisons: all in Libra—Epsilon (5·08), Xi¹ (5·84), Xi² (5·63)

BETA LYRÆ

The remarkable eclipsing binary with two unequal minima in each full period. The range is 3·38 to 4·36, and the full period 12·91 days. It is extremely easy to locate.

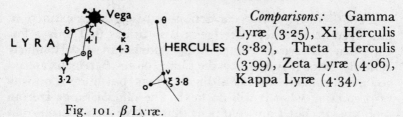

Comparisons: Gamma Lyræ (3·25), Xi Herculis (3·82), Theta Herculis (3·99), Zeta Lyræ (4·06), Kappa Lyræ (4·34).

Fig. 101. β Lyræ.

ALPHA ORIONIS (BETELGEUX)

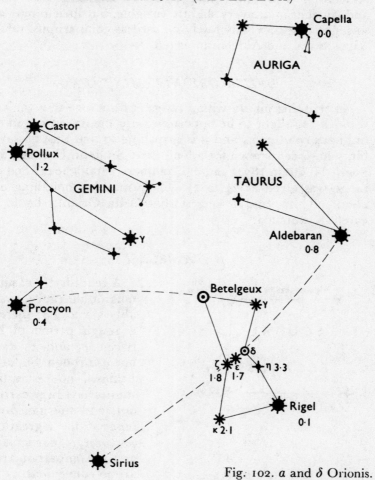

Fig. 102. *a* and δ Orionis.

Here there are always corrections to be made for extinction, and even at minimum Betelgeux is so bright that only a few stars can be used as comparisons. Aldebaran is particularly suitable, since it is of much the same colour. Betelgeux is said to have a rough period of around 5 years, but there is no way of predicting what it will do next. The official range is from 0·06 to 0·75, but I am confident that I have seen it drop to as low as 0·9.

Comparisons: Capella (0·05), Rigel (0·08), Procyon (0·37), Aldebaran (0·78) and Pollux (1·16). To be precise, both Rigel and Aldebaran are very slightly variable, but their ranges are so slight that they may safely be used as comparisons, taking Rigel as 0·1 and Aldebaran as 0·8.

DELTA ORIONIS (MINTAKA)

An eclipsing binary with a range of from 2·20 to 2·35. This is much too slight to be noticeable with the naked eye under ordinary conditions, and it is surprising to find that its variability has been known for a long time. Sir John Herschel first pointed it out in 1834, and in Chambers' catalogue of 1890 the range was given as $2\frac{1}{4}$ to $2\frac{3}{4}$. There may be something odd about all this, and I suggest that Delta Orionis should be carefully watched.

BETA PEGASI

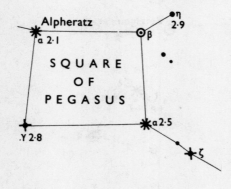

Fig. 103. β Pegasi.

A reddish star of small magnitude range, probably 2·2 to 2·8; there is a rough period of between 35 and 40 days, but it *is* rough. So far as I know, no exhaustive studies have been carried out, and the naked-eye observer has a great opportunity, particularly as the comparison stars are so convenient.

Comparisons: Alpha Andromedæ (2·06), Alpha Pegasi (2·50), Gamma Pegasi (2·84), Eta Pegasi (2·95).

BETA PERSEI (ALGOL)

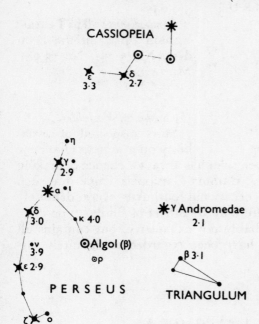

Fig. 104. *β* and *ρ* Persei.

The prototype eclipsing binary. Naked-eye observations are useful, as there are suggestions that the period is slowly changing. Algol has been fully described on page 73. Range, 2·06 to 3·28.

Comparisons: Gamma Andromedæ (2·14), Delta Cassiopeiæ (2·67), Zeta Persei (2·83), Epsilon Persei (2·88), Beta Trianguli (3·08), Epsilon Cassiopeiæ (3·33). Avoid the red irregular variable Rho Persei.

RHO PERSEI

This is a Red Giant irregular with a range of between 3·2 and 3·8. Avoid Algol at all times. My own rather sketchy observations indicate that Rho can drop to 4·0, which is below the limit given in the official catalogues.

Comparisons: Delta Persei (3·03; rather too bright), Eta Piscium (3·72), Kappa Persei (4·00).

LAMBDA TAURI

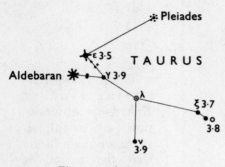

Fig. 105. λ Tauri.

An Algol-type eclipsing binary, with a range of from 3·3 to 4·2 and a period of 3·9 days.

Comparisons: all in Taurus: Epsilon (3·54; in the Hyades), Xi (3·75), Nu (3·94), Mu (4·32).

(b) Suspected Variables

Stars suspected of variability offer a great challenge to the naked-eye observer, who has always a chance of making an interesting discovery. Gamma Cassiopeiæ came into such a category before its occasional outbursts were definitely tracked down, and there may be others of similar type. The list given below is probably not exhaustive, but contains all the bright stars which have been regarded as definitely suspect.

BETA ANROMEDÆ

Official magnitude 2·02. It is a Red Giant, and so is under suspicion at once! It is so nearly equal to Alpha and Gamma that any marked difference between the three will indicate that something peculiar has happened, Beta being the most likely culprit. Beware, however, of local mist or cloud. Should you note that Beta is either markedly brighter or markedly fainter than Alpha or Gamma, check again after an hour or so to make sure that there has been no mistake.

Comparisons: Alpha Andromedæ (2·06), Gamma Andromedæ (2·14). It is interesting to note that in the last-century Harvard star catalogue Alpha was given as 2·1 and Beta and Gamma 2·2 each, while in the Oxford catalogue of the same period Alpha was 2·0, Gamma 2·1 and Beta only 2·2.

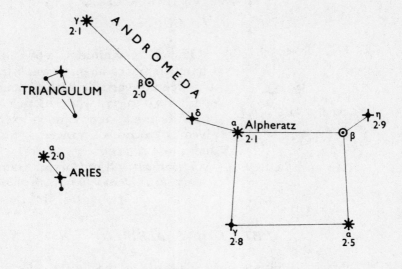

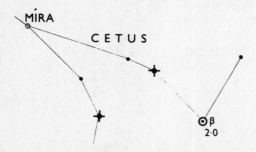

Fig. 106. β Andromedæ and β Ceti.

BETA CETI

Official magnitude 2·02, but it has been suspected of sudden short-lived rises to 1½ or thereabouts. Unfortunately it is isolated, and as seen from northern countries it is much lower down than any stars available for comparison, so that estimates are extremely difficult.

Comparisons: the only stars of real help are Gamma Andromedæ (2·14), Alpha Andromedæ (2·06) and Alpha Arietis (2·00). Fomalhaut (1·19) is much too bright.

BETA CORVI

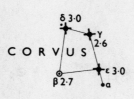

Fig. 107. β Corvi

Official magnitude 2·66. In Chambers' old catalogue it was listed as a definite variable with a range of from $2\frac{1}{2}$ to $3\frac{3}{4}$, while its neighbours Gamma and Epsilon were given as "suspects"; ranges $2\frac{1}{2}$ to 3 and 3 to 4 respectively.

Comparisons: all in Corvus: Gamma (2·59), Delta (2·97), Epsilon (3·04).

BETA CYGNI (ALBIREO)

Official magnitude 3·07. This star is the lovely coloured double. There is probably no real variation, though Klein, in the last century, suspected a very slow variation of from magnitude 3 to 4. I have watched it since 1937 without detecting the slightest variability.

Comparison: Gamma Lyræ (3·25).

EPSILON DRACONIS

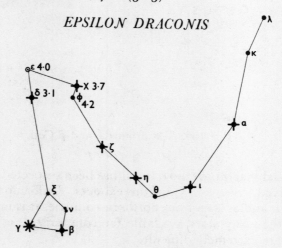

Fig. 108. ε Draconis.

Vega

Official magnitude 3·99, but once thought to vary slowly between 3¾ and 4¾. I have seen no sign of this since I began observing it in 1937.

Comparisons: Chi Draconis (3·69) and Phi Draconis (4·24), which lie close together not very far from Epsilon.

GAMMA ERIDANI

Official magnitude 3·01. The nineteenth-century astronomer Secchi considered that it ranged between 2½ and 3½, but this seems highly dubious.

Comparisons: Beta Eridani (2·79), Delta Eridani (3·72).

BETA LEONIS

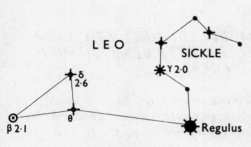

Fig. 109. *β* Leonis.

Official magnitude 2·14. Here we have a strong suspect, particularly since there is evidence that the star has faded by a magnitude since Ptolemy's time.

Comparisons: Gamma Leonis (1·99), Delta Leonis (2·57). Beta should be virtually equal to Gamma, but probably never drops far enough to be comparable with Delta even if it is variable at all.

EPSILON PEGASI

Official magnitude 2·31. Schwabe, in the last century, claimed that it varied between magnitude 2 and 2½ in a period of 25¾ days, but this remains totally unconfirmed, and even if there is a slight fluctuation the range is certainly much smaller than Schwabe supposed. Alpha Pegasi is the only really convenient comparison, though Gamma Cygni may also be used if necessary.

Comparisons: Gamma Cygni (2·22), Alpha Pegasi (2·50).

GAMMA SAGITTARII

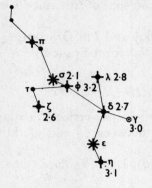

Fig. 110. γ Sagittarii.

Official magnitude 2·97. It was once thought to have a period amounting to years, and a range of from 3 to 3¾. It is not easy to watch from Britain, owing to its low altitude, and it seems unlikely that there is any real variation.

Comparisons: Delta Sagittarii (2·71), Phi Sagittarii (3·20).

ALPHA URSÆ MAJORIS (DUBHE), ETA URSÆ MAJORIS (ALKAID) and BETA URSÆ MINORIS (KOCAB)

All these three well-known stars have been suspected of slight variability, though apparently on the slenderest evidence. Their official magnitudes are respectively 1·81, 1·87 and 2·04.

Comparisons: Epsilon Ursæ Majoris (Alioth) (1·79) and Polaris (1·99, though itself very slightly variable).

DELTA URSÆ MAJORIS (MEGREZ)

There are very strong suspicions that the famous Megrez is variable, as well as having faded since ancient times, though the range and period—if any!—are not known. The official magnitude is 3·30, but there may be occasional falls to about 3¾.

Comparisons: Kappa Draconis (3·88), Lambda Draconis (4·06), Alpha Draconis (3·64), Theta Ursæ Majoris (3·19), Omicron Ursæ Majoris (3·37), Psi Ursæ Majoris (3·30).

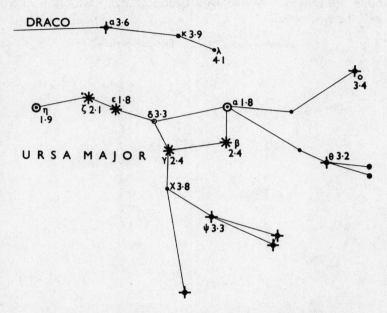

Fig. 111. *η*, *a* and *δ* Ursæ Majoris and *β* Ursæ Minoris.

ETA VIRGINIS

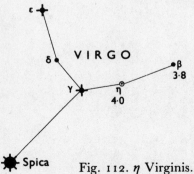

Fig. 112. *η* Virginis.

Official magnitude 4·00. Gould, a century ago, maintained that it fluctuated between 3 and 4, but this is unconfirmed and probably erroneous. I have certainly seen no signs of change.

Comparison: Beta Virginis (3·80).

When observing a naked-eye variable, allowance must be made for extinction unless the comparison star is very nearby; this has been pointed out in the text (p.229). The closer a star is to the horizon, the more of its light will be lost. The following table gives the amount of extinction for various altitudes above the horizon. Above an altitude of 45°, extinction may safely be neglected.

Altitude in degrees	Extinction in magnitudes
1	3
2	2·5
4	2
10	1
13	0·8
15	0·7
17	0·6
21	0·4
26	0·3
32	0·2
43	0·1

ASTRONOMICAL PHOTOGRAPHY

MOST PROFESSIONAL ASTRONOMY is now carried out by photographic methods, using complex equipment together with large telescopes. Without a telescope, one's scope is naturally limited, but interesting pictures may be taken with nothing more exotic than an ordinary camera.

If you point a camera towards the stars on any dark, clear night, and give a time-exposure, you will record star trails. As the stars crawl across the sky, they will leave their trails on the plate or film; the longer the exposure, the greater the length of the trail. Whole constellations can be photographed, and with well-marked patterns, such as the Great Bear, there will be no trouble about identification.

The star-trail photographs given in this book (Plates I, II*b*, and III) were taken by Robert Aylott, using a Japanese Yashica—but any camera will produce results so long as it has a time-exposure device. Remember to focus on infinity; a lens-hood is helpful for cutting out undesirable light (street-lamps, for instance) and great care must be taken with developing. Aylott has found that a good film-speed is in the region of 400 ASA; for a five-minute exposure it is best to use f/3·5, increasing to f/4 for a ten-minute exposure and f/5·6 for a twenty-minute exposure. These values do not have to be precise, but will serve as a general guide.

The Moon and planets also leave trails, and unusual conjunctions give spectacular pictures. Bright auroræ may also be photographed with an ordinary camera. Meteor photographs may also be obtained, and can be both interesting and spectacular.

Useful photographic work with a standard camera may be carried out with meteors and artificial satellites. If one of these moving objects happens to flash across the region being photographed, it will leave a clear trail—in which case the time of its appearance should be carefully recorded. Bright satellites, of course, may be deliberately sought. A good photograph of Echo II, taken by Henry Brinton with a Japanese Canon camera, is given in Plate XII.

247

Appendix III

BOOKS AND SOCIETIES

THE ENTHUSIAST WHO has no means of obtaining a telescope can at least derive enjoyment from keeping abreast of
what is happening in the astronomical world. Many cities,
both in Britain and the United States, have local societies,
listed in the annual *Yearbook of Astronomy* published in London
by Eyre & Spottiswoode and in New York by W. W. Norton.

So far as books are concerned, I propose to be brief. The
best star atlas available is undoubtedly the classic *Norton's
Star Atlas* (Gall and Inglis, Edinburgh). People with field-
glasses will enjoy *Astronomy With Binoculars* (James Muirden:
Van Nostrand), while I hope that those who want to do some
systematic observation will find something helpful in my own
book *The Amateur Astronomer* (W. W. Norton, The Amateur
Astronomer's Library).

INDEX

249

MONTHLY STAR MAP REFERENCE TABLE

	1800 hrs	2000 hrs	2200 hrs	Midnight	0200 hrs	0400 hrs	0600 hrs
January	11	12	1	2	3	4	5
February	12	1	2	3	4	5	6
March	1	2	3	4	5	6	7
April		3	4	5	6	7	
May		4	5	6	7	8	
June			6	7	8	9	
July		6	7	8	9	10	
August		7	8	9	10	11	
September		8	9	10	11	12	
October	8	9	10	11	12	1	2
November	9	10	11	12	1	2	3
December	10	11	12	1	2	3	

The table indicates the appropriate Star Map for any time and month of the year, the left-hand column gives the month of observation, while the vertical column represents the time of observation to within the nearest two hours. By simply reading across and downwards the required Star Map number can be located; thus the appropriate Star Map for a midnight observation during February will be number 3.

The Star Maps will be found on the following pages:

Star Map	Page Number		Star Map	Page Number
1	55		7	113
2	84		8	136
3	87		9	138
4	90		10	140
5	107		11	158
6	110		12	160